Whessoe

Whessoe

Two Centuries of
Engineering Distinction

Dennis W. Hockin, I.Eng., M.I.Mech.I.E.

The Pentland Press
Edinburgh–Cambridge–Durham

First published in 1994
by The Pentland Press Ltd
1 Hutton Close
South Church
Bishop Auckland
Durham

British Library
Cataloguing in Publication Data
A Catalogue record for this book
is available from the British Library

ISBN 1-85821-223-5

Typeset by Carnegie Publishing Ltd., 18 Maynard St., Preston
Printed and bound by Antony Rowe Ltd., Chippenham

Contents

Illustrations

Acknowledgements

Section Two of this historical account was intended to portray not just the structural and product changes of Whessoe but the changes in working conditions and working relationships during the fifty year period.

As explained in the preface, I have depended to a large extent upon my own personal memories but it could not have been written, with any degree of accuracy, without the invaluable help of many Whessoe colleagues, past and present, who provided additional comments, anecdotes and documents from their personal store.

My thanks are given to all those people especially, Trevor Brown, Malcolm Burke, Ian Davie, Karen Dean,John Dinsley, Margaret Dixon, Andrew Foster, Andy French, Cliff Glasper, Bill Lawson, George Metcalfe, Liz Penman, John Tate, Colin Turner, Charles White, Dick Wilson, and Donald Wood.

My special thanks go to Chris Fleetwood our Chief Executive for the original idea and encouragement during its preparation, to Ken Mullen our Company Secretary for his enthusiastic interest and sponsorship in achieving publication.

Last, but not least, to my wife Eileen who has always supported me, despite being convinced that Whessoe was my first love, even after the "divorce" in 1992.

In recounting this history I have referred to many people by name who in my opinion had a direct influence upon my career.

I apologize for the omission of many other people who have been my friends and colleagues and who helped to make my life at Whessoe so pleasurable.

Preface

WHESSOE PLC is one of the oldest operating Groups of engineering companies in the country with its origins going back to 1790 in the town of Darlington in County Durham, England, where its Head Office remains today.

The Group in its 200 plus year history has designed and manufactured almost every type of engineering product from small castings for the Stockton and Darlington railway to Nuclear Power stations, changing its direction and management techniques to meet the product demands of any particular period of time.

The 1990s have seen the most significant change in Whessoe's overall structure with an almost complete move away from heavy engineering fabrication to light engineering in the form of Instrumentation Control and Piping Systems with a world-wide involvement.

This structural change involved the closure and demolition of the Darlington Works where much of Whessoe's history was made and with Whessoe having been a significant integral part of Darlington for the last 200 years, employing as it did at its peak over 2,000 local people in its Works and Offices it would be wrong not to set down in a logical and detailed sequence some form of business and social perspective so that Whessoe and its people are not forgotten, nor are their achievements, which have made such an impact and had such a major effect upon this nation's engineering advancement.

This book, simply entitled *WHESSOE*, attempts to set down as factually as possible as many of these historical events and achievements as possible, in a manner which is readily understandable and hopefully interesting to the non-engineer.

The closure of the Works and other Group facilities and the dispersal of many of the Company's highly experienced staff over the years has unfortunately resulted in the loss of many project and social records and much hard gained knowledge and experience.

Despite this it has been possible to put together a fairly factual record of Whessoe's complete history to date and this has been done in two distinct sections.

Section One covers the first 150 years of Whessoe from its origin in 1790 to 1940 the first significant year of the Second World War.

The data for this has been taken from archival documents stored in the Durham County Hall but mainly from updated details researched and documented by G A Petch and R P Wood in 1950.

Section Two covers the fifty year period from 1942 to 1992 and has been written more as a social perspective of Whessoe as seen through the personal experiences of the author who was employed by and involved with the Company for that full period.

As this section is almost an autobiographical account it was only possible to give precise details for the areas in which the author was actively employed, so some licence has been used in fleshing out the other significant areas, relying on available records and information passed on by colleagues past and present.

Apologies are offered for any obvious errors perceived by experts but the book should be seen as an overall perspective and not an engineering thesis.

Foreword

Imagine the author, younger by a few decades, returning home from a job in Scotland, his bedraggled suit complemented by ruined shoes, the flapping soles destroyed by hydraulic fluid, shattered by having worked around the clock for a full week-end but satisfied with success. This story, just one of Dennis's many experiences with Whessoe re-counted with humour and insight, prompted me to suggest that he should write a permanent record. The narrative you are about to read, written after countless hours of research, is the end product.

To me the book is more than just a history of Whessoe for it deals with the fascinating social changes that have taken place in industrial Britain throughout the last fifty years. The fact that this is largely a personal account makes it no less relevant or reliable. Dennis has retained, even in retirement, a deep sense of involvement with and interest in the company and a particular feel for the people who worked for it. Few have enjoyed a career with a single company that is quite so varied or, with a span of fifty years, quite so long; these qualities make him the deal person to produce this historical record.

Whessoe is one of only a handful of companies that can claim a history of more than two hundred years. I still find it hard to grasp that the company, which was forged in the fires of the Industrial Revo-lution, is now in its third century. Whessoe, as a heavy engineering company, has seen and indeed been heavily involved with the devel-opment of railways, the rise of the petrochemical industry, town gasi-fication and nuclear power. Always a pioneering business, Whessoe has often worked at the forefront of technology, designing and building products to a quality that others aspired to. The Group has benefited from a number of visionary executives that have steered it through a changing and increasingly complex industrial and economic environment but whatever they achieved it was through the continuing loyalty, support and craftsmanship of the many thousands of people employed by Whessoe throughout its long history.

The company continues to evolve, heavy engineering has given way to instrumentation and electronics and with operations in Australia, France, Italy, Norway and the United States, as well as the UK, the Group has become truly international. It will nonetheless continue to have a special meaning to many of the people in Darlington, for it was here that the company laid down its deep roots.

But this is much more than a conventional company history, the thorough research combines the company's achievements over two distinct periods with poignant glimpses into past social attitudes. Above all it is written with warmth, sincerity and good humour, strongly supported by a wealth of illustrations. The book will appeal to all those who have been connected with Whessoe and to many who have an interest in social history.

Chris Fleetwood, The Whessoe Group Chief Executive

SECTION ONE
WHESSOE
The First 150 Years

1790 to 1940

The Origins of Whessoe

Whessoe traces its origins to an ironmonger's shop which was opened in 1790 in Tubwell Row in the very centre of Darlington by a Quaker, William Kitching. From this small beginning sprang the Whessoe of today, an international group of companies which currently employs over 1,500 people in manufacturing plants, construction sites and offices.

Nowadays Whessoe's interests are concentrated upon Instrumentation and Control, Piping Systems and Project Engineering with a continuance of site construction, but its reputation was built upon the design, fabrication and construction of storage and treatment plant for the oil, gas and chemical industries, wind tunnels, nuclear reactor vessels, hydro electric power and irrigation systems with a slight foray into the manufacture of plastic pressure vessels, beach huts and catamarans.

Over the period of time there have been considerable changes in the type of work, in the customers and correspondingly in the men controlling the Company's affairs and there have been several distinct periods in the development of Whessoe.

The first period stretches from the opening of the ironmonger's shop until 1830, the year when the Railway Foundry was established. The new Stockton and Darlington Railway, with the creation of which the Kitchings had been concerned, became a new and important customer.

The second period, during which locomotives and rolling stock were made for the railway, ended in 1862. It was in this period that the foundry, the third owned by the Kitching family, became known as the Whessoe foundry, deriving the name, which is of Saxon origin, from Whessoe Lane (still known as Whessoe Road) which ran past it. Records show that a Saxon village of that name existed over 800 years ago about one and a half miles north of the present site.

Thereafter, and until 1891, the Whessoe Foundry turned its attention to the structural side of railway work, its third phase of development.

The year 1891 saw the start of the fourth period and the beginning of the modern Whessoe, for in that year the business was converted by the proprietors into a private company and, in the decade that followed, Whessoe turned away from the general structural steel work it had previously manufactured to the building of gas-holders and also of tanks for the nascent oil industry.

The fifth period in Whessoe's change and growth began in 1921 when a public company was formed and when the company started in earnest to provide the technical basis for its services and to expand those services to meet the requirements of the particular industries with which it was concerned. This period took Whessoe right up to the start of the Second World War when product lines and customers changed once again. The wartime period can be classed as the sixth period of development.

The Beginning

During the first sixty-five years of its existence the business that was to become known as "Whessoe" was under the control, first of William Kitching, a man of strong Quaker beliefs and concerns for mankind, being particularly forthright in his demands for the abolition of slavery, then of his sons, Alfred and William.

The opening of the shop was a courageous venture, for William Kitching was a weaver by trade and in 1790 had a family dependent upon him. But it was a successful venture and the foundry, from which Whessoe really springs, was opened in 1796. At first the shop sold various ironware and some glass. In the foundry small repair parts were cast. Chimneys, cistern covers, and other goods were made and farm gear repaired. Additionally, some millwright work was carried out for local concerns.

When William Kitching died in 1891 he left a sound business able to support his family, and what is perhaps more important, able to provide a starting point for his two sons, William and Alfred.

At this time the campaign to establish the Stockton and Darlington Railway was at its height and the Kitching family played an important part in it. Initially, in the early days of the attempts to put a bill through Parliament to provide for this enterprise, it was seen as an attempt to provide better transport facilities, an ambition which was shared by the founder of the firm.

As the campaign reached fruition in 1821 William Kitching, the younger, subscribed £400 and in 1823 had the honour of being elected to the General Committee and also to the small working sub-committee which had day to day control of the work.

Darlington Market place circa 1843. The bow fronted shop on the corner, next to Davis & Co. is that of W. & A. Kitching, ironmonger and iron founder. The foundry was at the rear of the shop. William Kitching, son of the William Kitching who founded the business is 1790 is seen in the shop doorway.

To the Kitchings this was not merely an enterprise to which they had subscribed time and money. It was also an opportunity for business. Step by step, the Kitchings took on work from the railway. Their first contract, in February 1824, was for fifteen guinea's worth of nails which were used to fasten the iron chairs onto the sleepers. A few months later there was another order for nails, this time in greater quantity. Then, a year after the first contract, William won an order for supplying five tons of iron of various size for wagons, and, so the orders continued. But first came the opening of the railway. It is interesting at this point to recall that the day before the official opening six of the Railway directors took part in a trial run from Shildon to Darlington. One of the six was George Stephenson; another was William Kitching.

The success of the railway meant not only increased work for William Kitching as a director of the railway company, it also meant increased work for the foundry, and indeed by 1831 it was clear that the foundry in Tubwell Row was too small for the business available to the Kitchings. Since the foundry site in the centre of Darlington did not permit expansion the obvious step was to build a new foundry specifically for railway work. Perhaps one other important factor influencing this decision was the growth to manhood of Alfred Kitching, William's younger brother, who was perhaps even more interested in the foundry and its possibilities than William himself.

The Railway Foundry

The site chosen for the new foundry was a mile to the north of Tubwell Row, and adjoining the main Stockton to Darlington line. From the first it appears that Alfred had the daily management of the joint concern, while William acted as treasurer and kept the Tubwell Row shop and foundry open. It was Alfred's dynamism and his concern for detail that carried the foundry to success. He insisted on good workmanship alike from suppliers and from his own foundry. Early signs of Whessoe's "Total Quality Concepts".

Alfred sought to keep in close touch with his employees and develop in the works that same spirit of loyalty which he himself felt towards, not only his business but, to the new industry he served. His selection of employees and the assistance he gave them are pointers to this.

On the basis of this active loyalty and hard work Alfred worked with a single-minded vigour to increase the turn-over, expand the foundry's markets, and establish a reputation for reliability and quality. Gradually, his energy built up a market which, though still local, was far beyond the capabilities of the Tubwell Row foundry.

Though the railway took most of his products, not surprisingly since the railway was the foundry's reason for existence, Alfred took work from the collieries, the local gas-works, and the mills in the neighbourhood.

The early orders from the gas-works are interesting since Whessoe retained its interest in this industry for over 100 years. In those days it was mainly pipes and other castings which the Kitchings supplied. But this connection, and others, paled beside that of the railway and it was to serve this industry that Alfred Kitching bent his efforts. First came the orders for iron wagon parts, for repairing turn-tables, and for engine parts. But this did not satisfy Alfred. Before long he was actually making wagons and turn-tables and, most satisfying, the engines themselves.

Initially the goods traffic on the railway was let out to three people, Timothy Hackworth, William Lister, another Darlington ironmonger, and the Kitchings.

Under this scheme the engines owned by the railway were let to the operators who were responsible for any repairs. The Kitching's contract, in addition, laid down that, "should the Railway Company require new engines William and Alfred Kitching to be allowed to make one at contract price." This opportunity came in 1834 when one of the engines crashed and, in the course of repairs, the Kitchings were allowed to strengthen it and make it larger. This engine, re-named *The Enterprise*, was the first of some twenty-seven engines which the Kitching Foundry built over the next twenty-five years.

Perhaps the most famous of all the engines built at the Kitching Foundry was the *Derwent* which was completed in 1845 for the price of £1,160. It worked until the late 1860s on the Stockton and Darlington line and was then sold to a colliery where it ran steadily until 1891.

It was then presented to the North Eastern railway, and stood next to *Locomotion*, Stephenson's engine, on Bank Top Station, Darlington—a memorial to the Kitching Foundry and a striking example of how rapidly the design and construction of steam locomotives had developed in the twenty years between the building of Stephenson's engine and the *Derwent*. But this was not the last of the *Derwent*. In 1925 the *Derwent* was reconditioned and ran under its own steam in the Railway Centenary Ancient and Modern Procession. Trips were made between Darlington and Shildon, and Stockton at speeds of 12–15 m.p.h.

The Derwent locomotive was designed and built in 1845 for the Stockton and Darlington railway by Alfred Kitching at a cost of £1,160. It has been restored and rests now in the Darlington Railway Museum.

In 1970 the *Locomotion* and the *Derwent* were both moved to the Darlington Railway Museum and remain there to this day.

The *Derwent* was probably the first engine built while Alfred was in sole control of the works in name as well as in fact for at the beginning of 1845 he bought out his brother William. This step was not very surprising. Though William had given the Kitchings the entrée into the railway business, it was Alfred who had exploited this and transformed the foundry into one serving almost exclusively the railways and undoubtedly dependent for its prosperity upon railway work. It was he, too, who contributed, like Hackworth, though to a lesser extent, to improvements in the design of the locomotives used by the railways.

After 1845 Alfred pursued his own way. Despite his personal prestige and that of the foundry he did not attempt to get business other than was local. It is likely that his other interests prevented his being completely

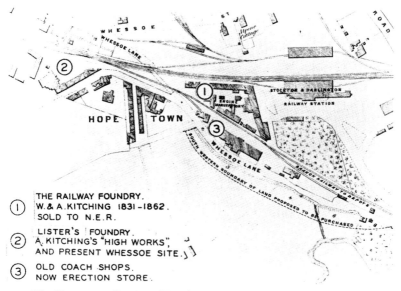

THE RAILWAY FOUNDRY.
① W. & A. KITCHING 1831 - 1862.
SOLD TO N.E.R.

LISTER'S FOUNDRY.
② A. KITCHING'S "HIGH WORKS",
AND PRESENT WHESSOE SITE.

③ OLD COACH SHOPS.
NOW ERECTION STORE.

*The Hopetown district of Darlington circa 1865 shows the early
Whessoe foundry and High Works site where Whessoe head office is still
based.*

absorbed in railway work and, though this is perhaps historically regrettable, it meant that when changes in the railway set-up occurred he was not over committed as far as the foundry was concerned.

These changes occurred in the late 1850s. The Stockton and Darlington Railway decided to take into its own charge, the re- equipping and maintenance work. Alfred had previously added the works of William Lister at the Hopetown foundry to the business. He reacted to the news of the change of railway policy by offering them his old railway works, and in 1860 this foundry was transferred to the railway.

At the same time Alfred decided to sever his own connections with engineering and he himself handed over the active control of the former Lister works to his cousin, Charles Ianson, though he retained a considerable interest in it. Thus ended the first notable period of Whessoe history.

The Ianson Period

Charles Ianson was a different type of man from Alfred Kitching. Like him a Quaker and connected with him by marriage, he had neither the same drive nor the same engineering ability. Though, in fairness, it must be said that he did not have available a new market equal in expansiveness to the railway which had given Alfred such scope.

In the event he turned out to be an excellent business man and did much to further the Company.

At first, though the business was called Charles Ianson and Company, Alfred retained some active interest and it was with his money that the old Lister works were adapted to meet the needs of the 1860s. It is about this time that the name of Whessoe first begins to appear in the term "Whessoe Foundry".

Charles Ianson was not, like Alfred, an engineer though he had been connected with engineering for some time.

From the first his activities were devoted to finding markets other than the railway for the Works. By now, indeed, the railway, which for over thirty years had been the main source of business, was more self-sufficient than it had ever been. There were no locomotive orders to be had, either for new engines or repairing existing ones. Moreover the railway was building all its wagons, trucks and coaches and keeping them in good repair. So the demand for what had been Alfred Kitching's two main stocks-in-trade had, so far as Whessoe was concerned, stopped altogether. Instead Charles Ianson and Company sought to retrieve some of the casting work done for the railway in the 1830s and 1840s but since given up very largely for the bulk manufacture of wagons and trucks. This policy was successful and a steady stream of chairs, switches, turn-tables and turn-table parts were made at the foundry.

An additional and important extension was to increase the amount of structural work which had started in the fifties, mainly for the railways. Though more heavy castings and structural work were made for the railway and used for bridges, stations and even hotels, Charles

Ianson extended the market and looked further than the local business that the railway provided.

An interesting example of his initiative was the extension of his structural work to piers. Though the records are scanty, evidence exists to show that Whessoe contributed to piers at Bournemouth, Plymouth, Aldborough, Hornsea and Redcar. For the first time too, work was exported, particularly to Spain and Portugal. Wrought iron columns were sent to such places as Huelva, Rio Tinto and Lisbon. At least one town in South America, Para, also took work from the Whessoe foundry.

At the same time new items for the railway were introduced and steps taken to increase the types of castings made for local collieries. The firm built up the semaphore type of signal into a speciality and certain improvements to the existing design were patented in the late 1860s. For the collieries the firm built pithead haulage machinery, including cages and made some improvements in safety devices.

But perhaps the most interesting developments came in the design and manufacture of steam cranes and weigh-bridges. Catalogues surviving from this time show a wide range of steam cranes ranging up to 20 tons. Weighing machines were also built and kept in repair by contract. Again, many varieties and sizes were made, the largest being the railway weigh-bridges with steel rails that went up to 50 tons. Perhaps the importance of this side of the Ianson business can be gauged from the fact that models from the weighing machine department were exhibited at the 1877 Darlington Industrial Exhibition. At the same time there was a useful demand for wrought and cast iron tanks, gas and water plant, and blast furnace plant from the rapidly developing Cleveland iron industry. These and many other items of manufacture provided considerable prosperity for the Company despite the loss of railway business and, throughout the 1860s and early 1870s prosperity continued.

During this time Alfred Kitching gradually withdrew from the business, notably after Charles Ianson's son joined the company as a partner in 1866, for James, like Alfred, was a mechanical engineer of considerable ability.

In the 1870s and 1880s however, there came a general and deep depression which hit the whole of British industry. Though Whessoe survived it did so in a weakened condition and without the three men who had raised it to some eminence and kept it there. Alfred Kitching died in 1882 and was survived by Charles Ianson for only two years. Within another year James Ianson was also dead. With their deaths not only Whessoe lost its personal drive but, so did Darlington. Alfred Kitching had, of course, done much to guide the town as a whole, while James did much for local education. Indeed it was said that it was his activities as Director of Studies at the new Darlington Technical College which overtaxed his strength and caused his death.

All three exemplified true Quaker principles in their own work and in the way they sought to influence their fellow townsmen. Darlington, as well as Whessoe, had cause to be grateful to them.

Whessoe Foundry Co. Ltd

For five years the foundry reverted to the control of the Kitching family and in particular to Alfred Kitching's youngest sons, Alfred Edward and Henry. However, in 1891 they disposed of their interests to Thomas Coates. In some ways it was a sad centenary of the day when William Kitching, ironmonger, had completed a first successful year in Tubwell Row, but in one respect it was fortunate. In Thomas Coates the firm found its second strong man, someone who was to pursue new markets and increasing expansion with the tireless, ruthless energy shown in the earlier years of its history by Alfred Kitching.

Thomas Coates had served with a number of engineering firms of standing in the North-East. It is clear that for him Whessoe was the "great opportunity". Though middle-aged, he was determined to abandon the security which his technical experience as an engineer could provide for the greater rewards and greater anxieties of ownership.

In April 1891 the Whessoe Foundry Co. Ltd., was registered with three subscribers, Thomas Coates and two associates of his called North and King. Initially the great difficulty was capital. Coates wished to reconstruct and re-equip the Works but he and his fellow directors could not raise enough money themselves. Fortunately the search for

someone to help in this did not take long and into the history of
Whessoe came H. S. Smith-Rewse.

Smith-Rewse joined the board in 1892 and it was he who gave Coates
the financial backing to transform the Whessoe foundry into a modern
firm capable of entering the twentieth century in prosperous condition.

The first market which Thomas Coates wished to re-enter was the
gas industry. This great and growing industry provided an opening for
making and erecting gas-holders and other plant, and it was in this
direction that Coates drove Whessoe. His first big order was for a
3,000,000 cubic feet capacity gas-holder at Gateshead and came shortly
after he had taken over the company.

Once this order was won. Coates began to seek more orders for
gas-holders. In the first five years of the 1890s Whessoe built gas-
holders at the rate of five a year. Coates also entered other sides of
the gas industry and Whessoe built all types of gas plant including

*Whessoe Foundry Co. Ltd designed, supplied and erected this 1 million
cubic foot three-lift gas holder with a steel tank 132 ft. diameter by 29 ft.
deep for the Tokyo, Japan Gas Company, circa 1900.*

condensers, scrubbers, purifiers, ammonia stills, exhausters, and oil gas plants. This work was not confined to the home market.

Gas-holders and other plants were built in Canada, Australia and New Zealand, Denmark, and France, countries with whose gas industries Whessoe had connections for many years.

Coates did not, however, drop all the lines which had been developed prior to 1891. He maintained the weigh-bridge department and many orders to the Ianson specification were carried out.

Considerable though this work was, the major achievement of Thomas Coates was to introduce Whessoe to the fast-expanding oil

Whessoe's entire commercial staff in 1899 comprised:
Back row – Tommy Adamson (chief estimator), Kit Bowser (clerk),
and Ian Black (cashier)
Seated – C. Snaith (buyer), John Crosby (chief clerk),George Clark
(clerk), and T. Hildreth (office boy).
The sons of C. Snaith and T. Hildreth were
also to become employees of Whessoe

*As you travel on the Edgeware Road–Baker Street extension section of
the London Underground you are protected by 50,000 tons of cast and
wrought ironwork supplied by the Whessoe Foundry Co., circa 1900.*

industry. This industry indeed represents the biggest factor in the history
of Whessoe.

Shortly after he took over the firm, Coates widened its connection with
the Anglo-American Oil Company, which had been set up as a subsidiary
of Standard Oil in 1888, and began to build tanks for them. Petroleum
tanks were built at Birmingham, Sunderland and Middlesbrough, some of
them being as large as 50 ft. in diameter and 30 ft. deep.

Already Coates was claiming to be *the* tank maker in the country
and one by one the biggest names in the oil industry of the day appeared
in the Whessoe order books. From the Whessoe point of view an
important introduction was to Marcus Samuel who in 1897 formed
Shell Transport and Trading. In the same year Samuel began to order
tanks and other equipment from Whessoe. The size of the orders placed
and destinations show that Whessoe must have made a large contribution
to the refineries which were being built in Borneo and the Far East.

By the turn of the century the oil industry was by far the largest of Whessoe customers.

On the basis of this work Coates and Smith-Rewse were able to enlarge the Whessoe Works, taking in adjoining land and buying more machinery for the Works. With this they were able to face with confidence the twentieth century and the tremendous growth in the oil industry that century was to see. Those who think that Whessoe's pre-eminence as tank builders is relatively recent can be reminded that as early as 1902 Whessoe produced tanks as large as 110 feet. in diameter and that the capacity of the tanks produced annually by Whessoe was in the region of 50,000,000 gallons.

The tremendous impetus at Whessoe at that time was undoubtedly from the Coates family. First it was Thomas Coates, then in 1910 his son Alfred was appointed Works Manager, and the following year Managing Director in place of his father. Kind to the men they employed, they nevertheless expected them to work as hard as they, themselves. It was indeed by example that the Coates family lifted Whessoe into the front rank of engineering firms in the North-East.

During the First World War the chemical industry began to be an important customer and this is a connection which has been kept up to the present day. Process plant was demanded in increasing quantity and was supplied by Whessoe in the form of shop-built vessels.

Equipping the Modern World

By 1920 the stage was ready for another change to Whessoe. The Coates family had built up connections with the oil, gas, and chemical industries. Using this as a springboard Whessoe was able to jump to the position of an engineering firm with a world-wide reputation. Those who followed the Coates were able to add a technical and inventive technique of the sort which Alfred Kitching had employed in the development of the locomotive.

Once again new capital was supplied—this time by the formation of a public company. The Whessoe Foundry and Engineering Company

Limited, under the Chairmanship of H. G. Judd and, following the death of Alfred Coates in 1924, a fresh and able mind was introduced to continue the work. The new Managing Director was R. B. Hodgson, an engineer of considerable standing in the gas and steel industries.

Hodgson saw clearly that the first task was to re-equip and change the Works to meet the needs of a highly competitive market.

At the same time C. M. Spielman the then London Director, had made an extensive visit to America. Both he and Hodgson had been much impressed by American views on mechanization and works planning. From this sprang a complete revision of the works layout which was capable of providing the tanks and other equipment needed by the oil industry and Whessoe's other customers.

Following this Works reorganization Whessoe stepped out in two directions. The first was to acquire a licence from the Chicago Bridge and Iron Company to manufacture Horton floating roofs and other evaporation saving devices required in oil storage. Then, in the thirties, under the managing directorship of Spielman, a new department was started to develop gas and chemical engineering.

This latter step led to the development of the Whessoe Woodall-Duckham electro-detarrer and the return of Whessoe to the forefront of manufacturers of gas plant. Alongside the development of the plant to be manufactured ran progress in actual manufacture.

In 1934, for example, Whessoe led the way in installing a pickling shop to remove mill-scale from tank plates etc. and so to make the tanks more secure against corrosion. This example was copied not only in this country but also in the USA, France, and elsewhere.

Perhaps even more important was the gradual change-over from riveting to welding which was sponsored by Spielman. Indeed, he made it a cardinal point in Whessoe policy and it proved to be a most important factor in the continued progress of the company.

By the outbreak of the Second World War Whessoe, then, was bidding fair to be considered one of the leading engineering companies in the country.

Whessoe continued to develop and change throughout the war and beyond.

SECTION TWO
WHESSOE
The next 50 years

1942 to 1992

1

Introduction

This Section has been written in an endeavour to recall the last fifty years of life in the Engineering Industry, but more particularly the history of WHESSOE as seen through the eyes of the writer as a Whessoe engineer.

To do this, it is written as an autobiographical account, and attempts to depict the changing face of Whessoe and working relationships during the period 1942 to 1992.

To put this period in perspective it is necessary to recall and relate the circumstances that led to the start of my career at Whessoe. The personal events depicted are in no way meant to appear as a hard luck story and it is hoped that the reader accepts that the earlier circumstances were typical of the times and could and did apply to many people through the period.

It should be understood, however, that throughout life a series of events and apparent coincidences tend to guide and direct the way one's life moves. I expect most of us have reflected many times upon the "what ifs" of life and thought how different one's career could have been except for certain, sometimes unconscious decisions taken at various stages.

Looking back over fifty years I have no obvious regrets about the way my life and career have been shaped by these decisions, in fact maybe if I had been "better educated" or "there had not been a Second World War" or "I had not worked at the Whessoe" then I probably would not be as content as I am now.

To set the scene of this personal history, my life in terms of this period of time, started in Hull in 1938 when I sat and passed my scholarship and had a few months of education at the Hull Riley High

School (Grammar School) prior to the declaration of War on the 3rd September 1939 (this apparently insignificant period of my life was later to have a marked effect upon the direction of my career).

During the two year period to 1941 Hull suffered badly from the wartime blitz and our school, along with several others, was destroyed.

After only nine months of Grammar School education I, along with the majority of pupils at Hull, either shared the remaining schools on a part time basis or received no education at all. As a 12 year old, of course, this was a marvellous event and no thought was given to future years.

At the end of 1941 my parents opted to move to a safer area and settled in Darlington which was a relatively peaceful place. Due to the lack of schooling unfortunately, I was unable to continue my Grammar School education and was placed in an elementary school in the north end of the town.

The level of education was very low in comparison with Hull but at least it enabled me to cope despite the missing period of schooling and at 14 years of age was ready to go out into the adult world with my formal education, such as it was, at an end.

A decision now had to be made about my future employment—where to work? What to do? These were decisions to be made without the benefit, in those days, of career teachers or advisers.

At this time there were three major employers in the town, who had the resources and were prepared to take on unqualified youngsters and put them through apprenticeships in craft, technical or commercial subjects.

These were Robert Stephenson and Hawthorns the locomotive designers and builders, the LNER locomotive works and the Whessoe Foundry & Engineering Co., known locally as STIVVIES, NORTH ROAD and the WHESSA. The three companies employed between them about 5,000 men, out of a Darlington population of 85,000, but despite that it was still almost impossible in those days to obtain work at any of those places unless your father, uncle, brother or other close relative had worked or did work at the firm and of course this didn't apply to me.

Fortunately, a neighbour had a friend who worked at the Whessoe and was prepared to put my name forward. His name was Bob Wilkinson, a time clerk, and a part-time conjurer with the stage name of Paxton Lynn and, although now long dead, well remembered no doubt by many current employees. This seemed the right contact. It was certainly going to take a good trick to get me a job at a time when the market was flooded with school leavers.

There was still one other problem of course, what sort of a job was I going to apply for? I knew absolutely nothing about engineering and, therefore, didn't really know which was the right branch to go into. That was, of course, if I got a chance at all.

In talks with my conjurer friend it turned out that his best contact was in the Fitting and Machine shops and that, therefore, was the logical route to take—and so my career as a Whessoe engineer took its first step.

Paxton Lynn performing another trick.

2

The Interview

An interview was fixed at 8.00 a.m. on a Saturday morning in late September 1942 with Mr. Harland the Senior Foreman in the Fitting and Machine shop. Saturday was a normal working day then, as part of a 48 hour week and I had to report to the Works entrance, in those days in Foundry Street, which led from the railway cut, still in use today. There were two other streets leading to Foundry Street, Alliance Street and South Street, each with rows of small houses. Foundry Street still had three "two up and two down" houses occupied and leading right up to the Works gates.

The gates were about 30 feet wide and were only opened at starting and finishing times and for the movement of transport. In 1942 the Works and Staff shared the same entrance, although at different times. A separate staff entrance, from Brinkburn Road running between a bowling green and tennis court, was not opened up until after the war.

At the left of the Works gates was a smaller door leading past the Time Office and it was to this entrance that I had been directed.

Regaled in a suit bought especially for the occasion and with my hair combed and teeth sparkling, I can recall just being able to see over the window ledge and explaining to the gateman that I had come for an interview.

A junior time clerk took me along through the Works to Mr. Harland's office and I was told to wait outside the door until told to go in.

I can still remember the feeling of dread when the door opened and a man dressed in a black suit and a bowler hat and who appeared to be almost 7 feet tall told me to come in and stand by his desk whilst he gave me an in-depth interview.

"Now son, can you tell me what half of one inch is as a decimal?" And then, "what is point two five of an inch as a fraction?" And again "what is three quarters of an inch as a decimal?"

These were very difficult question for a 14 year old with a shortfall in schooling (I still have difficulty with them today), but someone was looking after me that day and the answers popped straight out.

"Very good, son, start on Monday morning at the Big Office at 9.0 a.m."

I'd survived the interview with Ted Harland, who in later years proved to be the gentlest of men and very encouraging to the apprentices—more importantly I'd got a job at the "WHESSA".

3

The Office Job

On the Monday morning I promptly reported to the main office reception at 9.00 a.m. having passed once again through the Works gate, this time without having to report to the Time Office (I was a Staff man).

I was taken along to see Mr. Norman Park who was the Office manager and it was explained to me that as I was still only 14 going on 15 I was unable to start an apprenticeship in the Works until my 16th birthday.

Apprenticeships in those days were binding contracts on both sides, known as Articled or Indentured Apprenticeships and were for a fixed period of five years from 16 to 21 years of age.

For the next year therefore, I was given a position as an office boy or messenger. There were four other boys already employed at that time doing the same thing, waiting for apprenticeships or positions elsewhere in the office.

Our base was the Wages Department which also had a reception/enquiries window facing the entrance hall.

The five of us were given quite specific areas to cover throughout the Office and Works and after a week or two of getting to know the place I was told that my job and movements were restricted to the office block, based in the wages office which meant I looked after the enquiry desk and was the general "gofor" of the office staff. I was told that this was a coveted job and I had been given it because I was tidy and always smiling and this was supposed to be helpful when dealing with visitors to the enquiry desk.

We office boys however did not consider it to be a good job as one's movements were restricted and always under the eye of the senior wages clerk Mr. Robinson. The Works areas gave many excellent opportunities for losing oneself for an hour or two and it soon became apparent that I had not got the office job for my demeanour but had been manoeuvred into it by the more streetwise and slightly older boys.

The job itself actually was a good training ground for later life although the subsequent transfer to the Works with its totally different working conditions and environment was quite traumatic.

In the meantime normal life consisted of turning up for work in a nice clean office at 9.00 a.m. every morning until 12.30, an hour and a half for lunch and finish at 5.30 p.m. every day except Friday, when we finished at 5.00 p.m. and then Saturday morning 9.00 a.m. until 12.30. which gave a total working week of thirty- six hours, for which I was paid the princely sum of 12s. 6d. (65p) per week, once a month, in arrears.

My first job each morning was to help to distribute the mail around the office (after previously being sorted by others at 8.00 a.m.) On Monday mornings my second task was to wash out and fill up the Managing Director's (Claude Spielman) ink wells, clean his pen nibs, flush out and refill his special fountain pen, used only for signing letters and put clean blotting paper in his desk pad. This always had to be done in his presence whilst he cast a critical eye over you.

It was quite a frightening experience at the time but was accepted by me as the norm. I don't believe current MDs would get or expect the same service.

The rest of the days were taken up answering the enquiry desk, taking visitors to various offices, running messages for the wages staff and anyone else who could catch you.

On Thursday I helped make up the Works wages packets, and after several weeks was allowed to help pay out the wages from vantage points near the Works gates.

During this period the Works personnel were each given a board number which they retained for the duration of their employment. This number was painted on the top of a wooden board measuring 6 in. × 4 in. and the face of the board was chalked. Each day the man rechalked his board to give a clean white surface and wrote on it, in pencil, the details of the job he had worked on and the hours spent.

Each morning as the workmen filed passed the Time Office they shouted out their number, and were given their board, and a brass disc with their number engraved upon it, was hung on a hook to indicate that they were in.

Starting time was 7.30 a.m. and if you were five minutes late you lost quarter of an hour's pay, ten minutes late and you lost half an hour's pay and if you did not clock in before 7.45 a.m. you were not allowed into work that morning and lost half a day's pay.

The starting and finishing times were indicated by blasts on an untuned steam whistle which made it readily distinguishable from other factories.

At the end of the day the boards were all thrown into boxes on the way out of the gate and the time clerks, working amidst a miniature snowstorm of chalk dust at busy periods, then sorted them and recorded the details of work done and time spent per man.

From these details the cost of contracts and the weekly wages bill could be calculated.

Along with the board and brass disc each man had a small tin box with a lid and his number engraved upon it. Each Thursday the Works pay-roll was calculated down to the last halfpenny and collected from the Bank, after being counted and sorted into bags.

It was then the wages clerks job to put in each man's tin box the exact amount of his wages and at the end of the exercise every tin had to be correct. Precision was essential, one penny wrong and the whole exercise had to be repeated. Fortunately this did not happen too often.

Later, the tins were discarded and pay packets used. These were perforated so that the money could be checked without opening the envelope, but the boards and brass disc system continued until 1958 when they were replaced by Time Clocks which meant that a man was paid hour for hour.

One other very important job was to help the typists seal and stamp the mail, load it into a large leather satchel which was then locked and delivered to the post office in the town on an errand boy's bike just like Granville in *Open all hours.*

This sort of activity went on for several months until I was eventually moved to the Erection Department, which controlled all site construction work and was headed up by Harry Thompson, Arthur Nelson, Tom Scollick and Dick Parker.

At this time I was becoming more aware of, and taking an interest in, the Company and its activities.

The Whessoe Foundry during this period covered about 20 acres, bounded on the south side by Brinkburn Road, the west and north sides by the LNER railway works and the east side by the railway line to Bishop Auckland and Durham. At the south end there were a bowling green and tennis courts divided by a narrow tarmac path which led past the pattern shop and the Low Erection field up to the Main Office. To the right of the office was a private house occupied by the Woodwark family who acted as caretakers and general factotums.

Miss Woodwark the middle-aged daughter (she was probably only about 25 at the time) made the cups of tea for the Managing Director.

She walked across the yard each day at 10.00 a.m. and 3.00 p.m. carrying a tray with a white tray cloth on it. I remember this well as eventually I was elevated to this job, managing to upset the tea over the cloth on the very first day and although I got a good telling off I still had to do the job on occasion for quite a while.

To the right and behind the house was the pattern shop; there was also the compressor shop which maintained the portable air compressors, air being the main source of power in the Works. The shop doubled as a garage and general maintenance shop.

In 1940 the pattern shop was demolished and a new canteen built on its site, which had become necessary as the work load picked up and the number of employees, staff and works, increased to over 1,000. Many of these were women, brought in to do the work previously handled by men drafted into the forces. The women's jobs were principally crane-driving, welding, gas-cutting, fitting and assembling, painting, rivet-heating and general labouring.

During the war years, in particular, North Road employed around 3,000 men, Whessoe 1,000, the Rolling Mills 1,000, the Forge 1,000 and many others at small factories around the area. It was estimated that four times a day upwards of 5,000 men walked, ran or cycled along Whessoe Road, Brinkburn Road and Cockerton.

Children were all brought indoors 12.30 and 5.00 p.m. to avoid being accidentally trampled by the huge tide of humanity pouring down all the side streets on the way home for lunch or tea. It became so bad that eventually starting and finishing times were staggered between the factories.

Behind the compressor shop on the east boundary and running parallel with the main railway line and the old Stockton and Darlington Railway, was the foundry building dating back to 1850, when it was part of the William Kitching Foundry. The building was still in use up to 1940 when it was transformed into an assembly shop for fighting vehicle components such as flame-thrower turrets and Bren gun carriers.

To the north of the office were the fitting and machine shops, the plate and section shops, blacksmiths, press shop and tool room. To the west of the section shop was the engine house which contained a steam driven engine with a huge compression tank alongside. It also housed a generator which provided the Company with all of its own electricity. Further back still was the Ring, an open area of land used for the trial erection of tanks and vessels etc. The Ring was first established in 1934 and was so called because it was ringed by a rail track to take the steam cranes that provided the handling facilities. Finally there was the pickling and welding shops.

The products being made in the works at that time were all war related. Between 1914 and 1918 the firm did a considerable amount of war work but what was done then was completely dwarfed by the contracts undertaken for the 1939–1945 war, which was not surprising in view of the mechanization of the modern army.

Whessoe's largest contribution to the war effort was in oil storage tanks, landing craft came second in the list while AFVs (armoured fighting vehicles) came third.

First there were the desperate days of 1940 when invasion looked a strong possibility. Improvisation was the watchword and Whessoe began by fitting armoured box bodies to 200 trucks.

After Dunkirk, armament production was stepped up everywhere. Following the armoured boxes came the Matilda tanks. Whessoe took on the machining and preparation of armour and rear-end assemblies and in this way contributed to the building of 300 Matilda tanks.

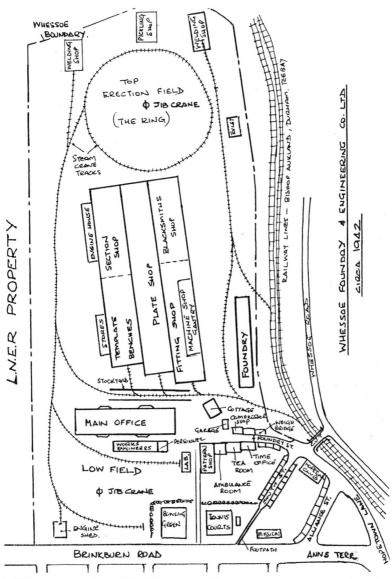

Whessoe site plan—1942. Ordnance Survey maps were not produced during the war, but this sketch provides an idea of the works layout before reconstruction in 1948.

The firm's biggest contribution in fighting tanks, however, was the production of all-welded tank hulls for the Churchill tanks. Whessoe built some of the earliest prototype models and were one of the first firms to get into production. We built well over 1,000 hulls—a very considerable number seeing that tanks of this heavy type were not required in such large numbers as the lighter tanks.

Whessoe was one of the first firms to produce the all-welded tank turret (previously riveted or cast) which was made in considerable numbers for the Churchill and Cromwell tanks.

The first orders for bombs came from the Air Ministry in 1936 and on the outbreak of war Whessoe got further orders. At that time they were the 250lb. type and during the war years we turned out a total of nearly 20,000. In 1943 and 1944 orders were received for the 8,000lb. "blockbusters" and the 12,000lb. "earthquake" bombs and Whessoe was one of only four firms in the country that turned out those types.

Whessoe also played a major part in the building of the Mulberry Harbour with five sets of shore ramp floats (the inshore ends of the piers), each measuring 60 ft. × 40 ft. × 10 ft.

Among other war equipment built by the Company were six-pounder anti-aircraft gun cradles and shields; pontoons for torpedo defence; several thousand gun shields for Browning and Marling guns for mounting on merchant ships; plant for gas production and storage and a number of high pressure vessels for hydrogen storage for the balloon barrage.

One thing Darlington was not known as was a shipbuilding town but, for war purposes, it undertook dry land shipbuilding. Nearly 100 craft of various types were built at Whessoe, including tank landing craft, gunboats, rocket ships and frigates and dredger pontoons.

These were prefabricated and taken by rail mostly to shipyards on the River Tees, where they were assembled and fitted out. They had their trial runs in the Tees before being handed over to the Admiralty complete in every detail and ready for action.

For the assembly and launching on Teesside a special company was formed by four firms which were doing the construction work. These included Whessoe and Cleveland Bridge Engineering Co. Darlington.

Despite the very large volumes of armaments and related products
that were going through the works during the war period, oil storage
remained the dominant product.

Wartime storage tanks built by Whessoe, a large proportion of which
were 118 ft. diameter, holding one million gallons of spirit each, had
a total overall capacity of 500 million gallons and these tanks were
erected in many parts of Great Britain including the Hebrides, Orkneys,
Shetland Islands, Faroe Islands, the Western Isles as well as Gibraltar
(where they had to be sunk into the Rock) and some were even shipped
to Murmansk in Russia.

Contracts for underground storage tanks, mainly for aviation fuel,
were received by the company as far back again as 1936 when the first
moves towards re-armament were being made and during the war more
and more of these tanks were being turned out at a rate sufficient to
provide additional storage for two million gallons every week.

Whessoe was probably the biggest builder of 12,000 gallon tanks.
These tanks 30 ft. long with a diameter of 9 ft. were the largest that
could be moved over British railways and were used for both emergency
and permanent petrol storage at most aerodromes. No fewer than 1,300
of these 9 by 30s were made for all the Services.

I was introduced to underground storage tanks during my period
with the Erection Department in 1943.

At that time we were working on a contract for underground petrol
storage tanks being fabricated and erected for an American Air Force
base at Greenham Common in Berkshire. This site of course featured
prominently in later years as the scene of CND rallies and Cruise
missile demonstrations, but Greenham Common remained in my mind
due to a personal involvement a few years later and was one of the
many coincidences of life previously referred to.

The underground tanks were fabricated in the Darlington Works and
then shipped to site by road transport. The transport was provided by
the USAF and consisted of massive multi-wheel vehicles notable in
particular for the drivers and crew who were all black Americans
wearing flying boots and sheepskin jackets and smoking enormous
cigars, which they gave out freely to the Whessoe men. Chewing gum

and chocolates were also special gifts which we office boys latched onto. The black Americans, being seen in the area for the first time aroused a great deal of interest but, I cannot recall any expressions of racial prejudice.

At this time although the Works were more understandable to me, they still didn't play an important part in my working life and I continued on with clerical work, although the time was fast approaching when my apprenticeship was due to start.

The office life was very comfortable, short hours compared to the Works 48 hour working week, two weeks holiday and many extra days at Bank holidays, tea and cakes at three o'clock and tips from visitors and office staff which supplemented my wage sometimes by as much as two shillings (10p) a week, equal to four visits to the cinema.

Why should I ever want to leave this environment and change it for the Works?

Inevitably the time came in November 1943 when my Indentured apprenticeship had to be signed, ready to start an apprenticeship on my 16th birthday in December.

For some unaccountable reason, despite offers from the Erection Department, Buying Department and the Traffic Office to stay with them, I pushed ahead with the Works idea and my parents and I signed a five year apprenticeship agreement with Whessoe Foundry and Engineering Co. Ltd. as a fitter and arrangements were made to start in December 1943 with my "old friend" Ted Harland.

4

The Apprenticeship

In December 1943 I left the offices, with some misgivings, and reported to the Fitting shop office at 7.30 a.m. on a Monday morning. At that time there was no such thing as a Personnel Department with a representative to make the transition from offices to Works an easy one for a youngster.

My interviewer of a year ago Mr. Ted Harland told me that I would be working for him for the next five years and that first of all I would need to buy some overalls and stout shoes. It was the responsibility of each man to buy his own working clothes and to clean and repair them.

He then took me along to the tool room at the end of what was then the Bomb room and introduced me to Mr. Rocket who would look after me and give me some work to do.

It turned out that Mr. Rocket was in fact another apprentice some ten months older than me and the fact that he was introduced as Mr. Rocket has been a standing joke between Ray and me ever since. We crossed each other's paths many times throughout our careers and in fact we finished up working together again in our final years at Whessoe.

That day was the start of fifteen years on the shop floor at Whessoe, with a lot of good times and a few bad times but always interesting and varied with many changes both in industrial relations and the working environment.

Whessoe Foundry, although having been established at that time for 153 years and considered to be one of the foremost heavy engineering companies in the north of England, in common with other major manufacturers of the time, had many faults in comparison with the present day.

There was no pension fund for the labour force, no sick pay, no canteen or washing facilities. There were long working hours (48 hours minimum), short holidays (1 week per year) and no apparent organized apprentice training scheme at all, although Articles had been signed which committed both sides to five years training, this normally being organized by the foremen on the shop floor. Detailed job training and achievement analysis came much later.

The rates of pay were very low both for staff and works, in fact Whessoe had the sad reputation for many pre and immediate post- war years of having a poorly paid workforce and was remembered as much for this as for any of its engineering achievements.

Why then were its employees so loyal? And loyal they were! A question worth asking but difficult to answer.

It must be said in mitigation and with the benefit of hindsight that there is no documented evidence of Whessoe's position in the league table of wage levels compared with other local companies. But discussions with some of the "old hands" both works and staff brought forth confirmation of historically low levels compared with other local industries.

In the 1940s there was a fairly strong union influence in the engineering industry that had been gathering strength during the 1930s in particular, but the central committees of the unions were based in London and all negotiations were made on a national basis. This gave them considerable bargaining powers for wage negotiations etc., but the resolution of minor problems was left to the local branches. There was a branch for each union in the town and we were obliged to pay our contributions there once a month but in my memory there was a great deal of apathy amongst the members and the branch officials had very little involvement in Whessoe internal labour problems.

Each craft union in the Works had a senior convener who negotiated with the Works manager on any local working conditions problem. Only pay rises and holiday entitlements were negotiated nationally.

I think it is fair to say that during the 15 years of my life on the shop floor, despite the poor working conditions, there was very little industrial action or reaction, particularly during the war years when every one gave of their best and worried very little about the worker/management battle that was inherent in all heavy industry. There is no doubt in my mind, however, that the working man at that time had good cause to resent management attitudes, and the working conditions in general, throughout the Engineering industry.

There was always present of course, the other side of the coin, in that the working man had a contribution to make to the dissension by way of inflexible working practices and demarcation between trades. These became far more predominant in later years, however, as unions became stronger.

A lot was learned by both sides during the war years but the pendulum was gradually swinging in favour of the labour force throughout the country, bolstered in 1945 by the advent of the Labour Party as the new Government in the post-war years.

The industrial unrest during the 1920s and the 1930s was due in the main to the repression of the labour force by management, particularly private owners. This was exacerbated by the depression and massive job losses which allowed employers to continue to dominate labour.

Right up to 1938/1939 prior to the outbreak of war, Whessoe had, like others, a system of hire and fire with workers queuing outside the gates hoping for jobs. Those in work were often laid off every other week and many foremen and supervisors used their authority to ride rough shod over the men.

This period, however, was just before my time and by 1942 the war effort provided more than enough work to take people's mind off the recent past. Subsequent discussions with retired workers, however, have enabled me to get an understanding of the earlier working conditions that eventually generated the labour unrest in the 1960s and 1970s as unions became much stronger.

The working conditions that prevailed at Whessoe in 1942, at the start of my working life, are probably well worth airing, even though they were accepted as the norm at that time. Even so, it was not so much the conditions themselves as the odious comparison with those that applied to the office workers that was the root of much of the resentment.

In the early 1940s Whessoe employed around 750 labour and 150 staff. About 50 per cent of the workforce worked outside, without any cover, throughout the year, winter and summer alike for six days a week. The only sources of warmth were coke braziers sited in various areas around the Works. They also served as canteens, each man brought his own enamel tea can from home and this was heated up at break times on the braziers. Although there was not a canteen as such there was a tea-room near the Works gates which provided tea from an urn, but this could only be used at lunch time for those who didn't go home.

As I stated earlier, foremen in those days had almost total power and one of the most noted of these at the time was the boilersmith foreman who ruled his men with a rod of iron. He was reputed to sack men at the drop of a hat and when something really irritated him he was known to walk round the yard and knock all the tea cans off the coke braziers, thus depriving the men of their morning break.

One of the stories going around about him was that each morning he would pat every man upon the back and from that touch he could tell to a second how long they had been standing by the coke stoves.

From the site plan of the 1940s you will see a small toilet block to the east of the site. This was the only toilet for the 750 men and it was what was known as a four-holer. It was strictly regulated with a permanent attendant and when you needed the toilet you knocked on the window and you were given two pieces of toilet paper and a brass disc. The paper you kept, the brass disc was hung on a board outside. Once the disc was hung up you were allowed five minutes in the toilet and if you took longer you could lose a quarter of an hour's pay. Also, you were allowed only two visits a day.

It should be borne in mind that there were no washing facilities provided, either before entering the toilets or leaving. It was 1950 before decent toilet and washing facilities were made available to the workmen, although extra provision had to be made for the women workers who started to arrive in 1940.

Even these conditions provided a source of fun for apprentices. As explained earlier, the toilet was a four-holer which mean it was a stone trough with four compartments each having a modesty door extending from your chin to your knees. A favourite trick was to occupy the first compartment and just before leaving, light a piece of oily cotton waste and float it down the trough—nobody was "quarter-houred" on those occasions.

As you will realise the men became quite hardy after being exposed to the elements for several years although of course many did succumb to colds, flu' and similar illnesses.

This presented quite a problem particularly for married men with families as the Company did not provide any sick pay for the workmen and the National Insurance scheme, which started in 1946, paid out only after a full week's sickness, with the first three days absence being excluded.

In 1949 the National weekly sick pay was 26s. for a man plus 16s. for his wife and 7s. 6d. for the eldest child only. A total of 49s. 6d. for the week, needless to say absenteeism was very rare and men tended to work when quite ill at times.

In comparison with this the staff were paid full salary for a maximum period of one calendar month and even this was extended in appropriate cases. In addition to the full salary the staff were able to claim their National sick pay, which meant they were better off on the sick.

It wasn't until February 1949 that staff sick pay took into account the amount paid under the National scheme, after the first month's illness.

Prior to the introduction of the National sick pay scheme the men at Whessoe relied upon collections from their workmates in times of extended illness. In 1920 the men formed their own Provident Society, each paying sixpence per week into the fund from which payments were made to sick members.

In 1925 the Company agreed to contribute the equivalent of half of the members subscriptions, that is 3d. per week per employee.

The scheme was still precarious as late as 1951 when the Society's balance sheet showed total assets of £271 6s. and, because of a flu' epidemic they were paying out £37 per week, which meant the fund could survive only, for about seven weeks before it was insolvent. To counteract this each man paid a levy of 2d. per week for six months. The Company did not contribute any additional funds.

It was not until 1974 that the Company actually paid sick pay to the men that remotely resembled the staff scheme. Even then it only

paid 80 per cent of the National minimum basic rate less the full
National sick pay, with no payment for the first fifteen day's illness.

A retirement pension, or the lack of one, was another area of great
concern in the 1940s. No one in the Works, when I started, had a
pension at all and as a result many men continued to work past the
age of 70. They would have no means of support other than their
savings and possible collections from colleagues. It wasn't until 1949
that the executive management began to accept the necessity for a
Works pension scheme, despite the fact that the staff had a good con-
tributory scheme long before the war.

The management were lobbied for a long time by Works
representatives to approve a scheme to cover all workers. Eventually
in April 1950 a scheme did become operable based on a weekly contribution from each man of 2s. 6d. (12½p) and a Company contribution
of 5s. (25p) per week which, based on an average weekly wage of £5,
equated to 2½ and 5 per cent respectively.

The contributions and, therefore, the pension sums were not linked
to earnings and thus did not vary over the years.

A man became eligible to join the scheme at 24 until the normal
pensionable age of 65 and for his contribution of 2s. 6d. (12½p) per
week he would receive a pension of 1s. (5p) per week for each year
of service which entitled him after forty years, to a pension of 40s. Of
course, as the scheme did not start until 1950, it would have been 1990
before anyone became eligible for that maximum sum.

When the scheme started in 1950 anyone who was under 64 and
had a minimum of ten year's service would automatically be entitled
to a pension at 65 based on 8d. per week for each year of service,
which meant a maximum in that case of £1.6s.6d. As late as 1965 men
were retiring from Whessoe after fifty year's service with a derisory
pension of £2 per week.

This scheme and its maximum level of payment existed right up
to 1975 when in that year, and later in 1978, further improvements
were made. Finally in 1980 a scheme with contributions and payments
linked to earnings was introduced and merged with the existing
scheme.

Even then the payments and peripheral benefits fell well short of the staff scheme. I understand that as this account is being written the Staff and Works schemes are being equated—forty years after the original introduction of a Works Pension.

I have tried to give a fairly factual picture of the working environment that existed in the 1920s and the 1930s up to the outbreak of the Second World War, the major problems being poor wages, no sick pay, no pensions and of course a high level of unemployment. It may also go a long way to explain the "loyalty" to Whessoe.

If you needed work and you had no ready means of transport then you had to stay in your particular area whilst work was available. If you stayed with the same company you had a better chance of being recognised by foremen who did the hiring and, therefore, a better chance of being retained or picked from the queue outside the works gates when hiring and firing was the name of the game.

If you had a job you stayed with it as long as possible. You also encouraged your sons and other male relatives to apply for work at the same company as again they had a good chance of being employed on the basis of your reputation as a reliable worker and timekeeper.

In researching records and from my own memories there were several families employed at Whessoe from the late 1880s onward. Most notable of these was the Park family, who at one period had four generations at work at the same time.

When I started on the shop floor in 1943 there were seven members of the Park family working. George Park the father, two sons, a cousin, two uncles and two daughters.

George Park's father and his grandfather before him both had sixty year's service when they retired and George himself had fifty-three when he retired in 1950. A brother Dick retired in 1954 with fifty-five year's service and his son Ernie actually refused voluntary redundancy with a full pension in 1984 because he needed another year to maintain the family standard of fifty year's minimum service.

The numbers of tradesmen who served the full fifty years and more are legion but probably the best known was Rueben Simpson a blacksmith who had fifty-seven year's service and finally retired in

1950 aged 71 years. Even then he was a force to be reckoned with, I and many other rookie apprentices were sent on fools errands to the blacksmiths for two clips and got them from Rueben—one on each ear.

Finally there is on record a photograph of six men, taken in 1949, and still working, with 312 years service between them.

Despite my somewhat cynical explanation of company loyalty there is no doubt that the core of craftsmen, after a long history at Whessoe did develop a great pride in their own skills. They dedicated their lives to doing the best they could for Whessoe and in doing so built and maintained the foundations of the Whessoe Group to make it one of the foremost engineering companies in the country.

It was with this type of craftsman that I was taught my trade as a fitter, an experience that I would not have missed for the world.

Six long service employees with a combined total of 312 years service.
Back row—C. J. Hamilton, H. Carlton, J. H. Talbot, J. R. Park.
Seated—R. C. Simpson, G. E. Clark.

As I have said previously, there was no established training programme for apprentices despite the fact that we were Indentured apprentices. The training came from working alongside the old hands, who because of their natural dependency upon each other, developed in the recent bad times, had no reservations about teaching the boys everything they knew.

We learned not only the need for certain methods of working but also the tricks and quirks of the trade which produced both accuracy and efficiency.

It was accepted that apprentices made their own tools. This called for skill with a file and scraper that came only with hours of practise and again the occasional clip across the ear if you got it wrong too often.

Once the tradesman recognized that you had the hang of things you were given a job to do on your own, which usually was part of his week's allocated work and if you made a mess of it, it could affect his earnings. This helped to sharpen your mind and develop a confidence in your own abilities. They were not only good tradesmen but amateur psychologists as well.

Although there was no apparent system to the apprenticeship scheme we were all rotated over the various branches of our trades. As a fitter I learned not only fitting activities but the use of small lathes and milling machines, marking off and setting up plate fabrications ready for welding, as well as simple tack welding itself. All of this helped one to get a better understanding of the problems of associated trades.

In addition to the practical aspects of work, apprentices were expected to enrol for night school, three nights a week, which cost 10s. (50p) a term. This was reimbursed by the Company provided you passed the term examinations.

The first year's lessons were, from memory, basic arithmetic, English and science and then you moved up to technical drawing.

Craft apprentices were generally expected to achieve City and Guilds standards for their particular trade and if capable then move on to O.N.C. and H.N.C standard. Eventually a streaming system was developed so that the achievers could transfer to engineering apprenticeships with the possibility of being considered for staff positions if successful.

Many craft apprentices did pass O.N.C. and H.N.C. examinations but preferred to stay in the Works.

Template makers and toolmakers in particular achieved very high standards in geometry and trigonometry, which were essential subjects when developing extremely accurate templates and jigs for production work. I never ceased to be amazed by the mathematical ability some of the older hands had, despite being in many cases self educated.

I continued with my apprenticeship for the next two years moving from one area to another. After a short period in the new tool room I moved to inspection of 250lb. bomb nose and tail castings. This entailed weighing machined castings and checking the screw threads with NO/GO gauges to ensure the detonators and tail fins, which were made in another factory, fitted exactly.

At this time as the Company was completely on a war footing, all inspection was run by the A.I.D. (Armaments Inspectorate Division), a government inspection department whose staff were resident in the Works. The records they kept were meticulous and I suppose this was the start of Quality Control as we know it today.

Material movement was controlled by the Ministry of Supply and nothing could move in or out of the Works without Ministry approval.

The designs for much of the work was top secret and people having access to many of the drawings had to sign the Official Secrets Act, the level of secrecy being down-graded as the drawings were broken down into working sketches.

Following on bomb inspection, I moved onto the assembly of components for Bren gun carriers, tank landing craft and Churchill fighting tank hulls. These were fabricated and welded from two inch and three inch thick armour plate steel, demanding new welding techniques which had to be developed at Whessoe.

Welding, which was introduced to Whessoe in 1935, was still in its infancy but great strides were made during the war years, largely as a result of Claude Spielman's efforts, in not only improving our own techniques but in the development of new procedures to cope with the new materials. These involved pre-heating the steel, the use of multiple welding runs in thick steel and finally stress relief of the completed weld.

These early years enabled Whessoe to realize the future potential of welding and to have the foresight to spend considerable resources on research and development which eventually made Whessoe one of the foremost welding engineers of the post-war years.

Returning to the apprenticeship, the job I found most interesting was "marking off". This entailed taking rough castings, some weighing as much as 5 tons, supporting them on large cast iron marking off tables and levelling them using jacks and wedges so that lines could be marked on to allow the castings to be accurately machined. From this you rapidly learned to read quite detailed drawings and set up angles and centre lines, using to some extent, the geometry and trigonometry being taught both by the fitter and the night school lessons.

To mark accurate lines and ensure that they were visible during subsequent machining operations we coated the castings in whitewash mixed with glue size which made it semi-permanent. This mixture had several uses.

You will no doubt have realized that up to now there has been no mention of any of the staff employees other than the foreman. They did exist but we had very little contact with them during the course of a working day and I am sorry to say that, at that time, there was a distinct gulf between Works and Staff. Even the lowest clerk considered himself to be a class above a workman, and a draughtsman was quite a nobleman in comparison. It is interesting to develop this because it was part of the "Them and Us" syndrome that still exists in varying degrees today. The two are now generally referred to as "blue collar" and "white collar" workers.

The working man was really no different, as there were class distinctions within the Works. A fitter considered he was better than a boilersmith or a machinist and within the boilermaker trades the template maker was the elite.

In fact, in later years, my future wife's grandmother used to tell everyone that her granddaughter was courting a template maker. Even though she knew I was a fitter, to her it made it a much better match.

As I moved through the Company and came more into contact with the staff I realized that a lot of them really were not as smart as they thought they were. On the other hand many of them were exceedingly clever and pleasant to work with and had no airs or graces at all.

As time moved on and there were more transfers of Works to Staff there was a considerable levelling out of "class" structure.

There was also, of course, a better understanding of people in my own mind which obviously had been formed from past attitudes. I did have one or two bitter experiences of class distinction, however, which will be related in due course. Although they were very upsetting at the time they served to mould my character somewhat and I vowed never to look down on other people and to try to treat everyone the way I would wish to be treated myself.

I am not sure I ever achieved that but I would like to think so. It is a very good saying "Always be generous to the people you pass on the way up—they are usually the ones you pass on the way down". The many reorganizations in the Company and the phases of redundancies that took place in later years proved the point many times.

In the early stages of my apprenticeship, however, my little world was the shop floor and night school and how to spend my half-crown (15p) a week's pocket money.

I always seemed to be happy as an apprentice. We were constantly learning, not only our trades but also about human nature, although we probably did not realise it at the time. The men worked hard, had poor working conditions and not a lot of money but there was always time for a joke and a laugh.

First year apprentices, of course, were fair game and we all fell for the—"go to the tool room for a left-handed hammer", a "long weight" (wait), "a pound of steam to test the seams" and the punitive one I have already mentioned "couple of clips from the blacksmith's".

We also had, of course, our own way of retaliating. The burning waste in the toilet was one. Filling your mate's jacket pocket with scrap steel, so that he couldn't lift if off the coat hook, just as he was rushing to get an early place in the clock-out queue, was another". But the favourite one was the whitewash and glue size.

A draughtsman or an engineer who came onto the shop floor to check or correct a drawing, or I suppose any unsuspecting person, was considered fair game and was encouraged to stand near the marking off tables. Whilst in deep conversation one of us would crawl underneath and paint his heels with whitewash. Quite an entertainment to see them clip clopping back up the shop with spots of white flashing—no one ever told the victim until he got back to the office. By then it was too late for recriminations. A very childish trick but there again, children are all we were at 16.

As the time passed I moved on to other work, which included fitting the heavy hinges to the ramps on tank landing craft. This was always outside on the "Ring" and not very pleasant in the winter but great when the sun was shining.

There was an assembly shop for Bren gun carrier turrets in the old Foundry and although the work was easy the environment was not. The shop floor consisted of layers of compressed moulding sand, accumulated over 100 years or more and the sand had its own colonies of sand fleas which took every opportunity to jump up your trouser legs or your overall sleeves. It took several months to become inured to these bites—and we did not get any extra pay for it!!

As we continued to learn our trades and gain some further education at night-school, there were other activities going on and around in which apprentices were not directly involved, but are interesting to recall.

Darlington remained clear of the bombing raids that constantly threatened other areas. I believe only two small bombs were dropped on the railway works and some houses were machine-gunned by an enemy aircraft which had lost its way and was dumping what was left of its load. Despite this the town had to comply with all the war regulations, blackouts, fire watching, air raid precautions and the formation of a Home Guard Division.

Mr. Grant, who was General Manager at the time, became one of the senior controllers of the A.R.P. in the town and was responsible for much of its organization, particularly within the Whessoe Works area. All members of Staff and Works were required to take their turn at fire watching at night and week-ends. We were all also, subjected to lectures by full time A.R.P. officials, two of whom A.C. Morgan and A.J. Robinson eventually joined Whessoe at the end of the war as our first Personnel Managers.

The other interesting subject was the formation of the Home Guard. Whessoe had its own Battalion under the command of Major Claude Spielman our Managing Director and again every able bodied male over the age of 18 was required to join. Inevitably, it attracted all sorts of characters and my favourite story concerned a particular Whessoe character of the time, called Albert. Although I was not involved and I have not been able to locate any written account of the occurrence it certainly makes a good story typifying the personalities and attitudes of the time.

Major Spielman the C.O., a very able man who won the M.C. in the previous war, took his Home Guard very seriously and parades were held every week in front of the offices. On one particular day, in rehearsal for a big parade the C.O. called the Guard to attention several times and was never satisfied with the result. Albert dropped his rifle, whether by accident or in disgust, I do not know.

Major Spielman immediately ordered him to pick it up. Albert refused and told him, not too politely, what to do with his rifle and walked off parade.

Subsequently Albert was summoned to a disciplinary hearing and found guilty. (I told you the C.O. took his Home Guard seriously). There is no record of the actual punishment but I would imagine there would be quite a problem getting Albert to comply with that in any case. Nevertheless Albert continued in employment at Whessoe for many years and also continued to be what is kindly known as a "character," along with many others. I often wonder whether Stanley Holloway wrote his monologue about "Sam, Sam pick up thy musket" after hearing about Albert or whether Albert was emulating Sam. Although the above anecdote smacks of Dad's Army the Whessoe Home Guard was really quite a professional organization.

One other such character worth mentioning was Johnny who lived with his mother in No. 9 Foundry Street, one of the three houses still occupied near the Works gate, the other two incidentally being occupied by George Park and family and George E. Park and family.

Whessoe Home Guard; can you put names to faces?

These houses if you recall were "two up and two down" houses without benefit of bathrooms or hot water supplies. Johnny's job for many years as a labourer in the machine shop was to climb down into the pit under the big machines and clean out all the turnings which were covered in oil and, in the case of castings, with graphite. At the end of his shift Johnny, to say the least was dirty and try as I might I cannot recall his getting a wash during the many years that I knew him. He was obviously known to one and all as "Dirty Johnny" a title that he did not appear to be upset about and certainly never took offence at.

He was looked after by one or other of the machinists who fed him and when his mother died made sure he remained as healthy as possible.

When the new toilet blocks were installed in 1950 he was one of the first to be introduced to the showers and was literally scrubbed by his mates, but he soon returned to his old state.

Johnny was as tough as nails, however, and always refused to go to the doctor or dentist. On two occasions I have seen him sitting on an upturned crate next to one of the milling machines having a tooth extracted without the benefit of an anaesthetic.

Such was the stuff Whessoe was made of, from the educated and the ignorant, the nice and the not so nice, the dedicated and the not so dedicated, each and every employee, however, having some attribute or skill that made his employment worthwhile.

During this period of time although most of the jobs at Whessoe were reserved occupations some people were still being drafted into the forces and there seemed little rhyme or reason for the selection. In general, apprentices were excluded, but some were called up as soon as they were 21 and out of their time. Some were never called at all, others were called up in mid term.

For some reason King George decided he needed me much earlier and the month before my 18th birthday I received a letter inviting me to attend a medical for the R.A.F.

On the 15th December 1945 my apprenticeship came to a halt after completing two years of the required five and achieving a pass at S2 night school, one year short of achieving my Ordinary National Certificate (O.N.C.) in Mechanical Engineering. I had to report at a place called Padgate, the reception area for the Royal Air Force.

5

National Service

The period of time I spent in the R.A.F. (2 years 9 months) is not particularly relevant to this social history except that there were several occurrences that had associations with Whessoe and are worth recording.

After the registration and kitting out at the Reception Centre at Padgate, which took about two weeks, we were drafted to various training centres for eight weeks "square bashing". I was sent to, of all places, Greenham Common which was referred to earlier as one of the sites on which Whessoe had built underground storage tanks for the U.S.A.F.

Following the cessation of hostilities in 1945 the camp reverted to the R.A.F and became a training ground. Basically we were taught discipline, marching and arms drill and eighty of us in four huts were under the guidance of two drill instructors, one of whom, Corporal Carpenter, I was to come across again several years later under different circumstances through Whessoe.

After completion of the basic training course at Greenham Common we were posted to various trade training courses. Generally the rule appeared to be, if you had been a lorry driver in civvy street you were sent on a medical course and if you had been a nurse you trained as a lorry driver. If you had been a clerk you were sent on a fitters course, such was the perversity of the Armed Forces administration. Fortunately for me they slipped up and I was posted to an aircraft engine fitters course at Cosford near Wolverhampton, which enabled me, in some respect, to continue with my apprenticeship.

After a six month's course I was posted to a squadron at the Empire Test Pilot School near Farnborough. This was great fun as there was every type of aircraft available there and every nationality of pilot.

Apparently, after a few months, they became aware that I was enjoying it and I was once again transferred, this time to a Maintenance Unit near Crewe, which to all intents and purposes was like working back at Whessoe under factory conditions. Before long I was back on "marking off" and inspection of machined parts, which was useful experience.

After a couple of months though it became a bit boring doing the same thing every day. A fellow fitter, who incidentally had been a greengrocer in Wigan, suggested the two of us should volunteer for an overseas posting to Singapore, which was supposed to be the choice posting at that time.

Overseas postings in the R.A.F took priority over anything else and it only took three weeks to get ours. Because we had volunteered for Singapore my colleague went to Germany and I went to South Africa and we were never to meet again.

I went to Durban by troopship via the Suez Canal, which took four weeks. I came back almost two years later as a civilian by the Windsor Castle line, via the Canary Islands, which only took two weeks.

During my stay in South Africa I took some leave in what was then Southern and Northern Rhodesia and visited the Victoria Falls, a memorable sight. On a particular visit I crossed a bridge over the Zambezi River. Prominently displayed in the centre of the bridge was a notice board announcing that the bridge had been built in Darlington, Co. Durham, England. Even at a distance of 8,000 miles I couldn't get away from Darlington.

My stay in South Africa was again a very pleasant one and I can honestly say I enjoyed every day of my National Service. I met many different people and made many new friends. One of whom was a lad called John "Geordie" Adams from Sunderland. We served together for the full period in South Africa until we were demobbed. We lost touch with each other for about 10 years until he turned up again as a construction foreman for Whessoe, where he remained until his retirement in the 1980s.

6

The Return to Work

After my demob in 1948 I returned to Whessoe at a time and age when I should have been completing my original apprenticeship and earning "big money" (basic earnings for a tradesman at that time was £3. 10s. 6d!!)

Although I spent most of my National Service in a trade similar to my apprenticeship I was dismayed to learn that Whessoe, and indeed the Trades Union, did not accept this period as a genuine apprenticeship. I had to return to work under a Government sponsored Interrupted Apprenticeship Scheme for a further two years which meant that up to 23 years of age I would still be an apprentice and all of my earnings would be reduced by a statutory 10 per cent.

Whessoe obviously benefited from this saving but of course, like all other companies they had to take back into employment all of the men who had been in the forces during the war, as well as retain their current work force to maintain production flow. The return of the apprentices was seen as an additional national burden, although to the best of my knowledge there were only three of us at Whessoe.

The obvious things I noticed upon my return were the significant changes that had been made to the Works and Offices.

Evidently even as early as 1941/2 the Whessoe management had been planning improvements to the site. The volume production of the war work had highlighted shortfalls in continuity of operations and flow of materials. These had been carefully noted and the intention was to put in hand an improvement scheme as soon as the right situation presented itself.

In 1945 immediately after the cessation of hostilities, the then Chairman, Mr. Harold Judd signed the papers to set the project in motion.

7

The Reconstruction

The decision to reconstruct at all was based on the need to meet forecast national post-war plant refurbishment and expansion needs. It had become apparent from experiences gained during the war when trying to maintain production requirements with a 15 acre site, part of which was only leased, and with antiquated buildings and equipment, that considerable rebuilding was required.

By the mid 1940s the Works had grown up erratically. The main shops were built in 1928, the welding shop in 1938 and the foundry, milling shop and other buildings were of 1840 to 1860 vintage. The east side boundary wall was said to have been built by George Stephenson whose Stockton and Darlington railway ran alongside it.

The offices were built in 1903 and were too small and in the wrong place. Worse still the 30,000 tons of steel a year did too much travelling about the Works. Incoming steel travelled a circuitous route from the loco. shed past the main shops, around the Ring, finishing up at a gantry and stockyard too small to accommodate it.

During the war the main shops proved to be first class but needed some additional length. A number of smaller departments were either badly located or in unsuitable buildings. A typical example was the old foundry, which was being used as an assembly shop. Being over 100 years old it was of antiquated design and at the wrong end of the works.

The sheet (or plate) shop was also badly placed for receiving materials and it did not have any overhead cranes. The template loft was too far away from the marking off benches. The old milling shop, like the foundry, was yet another building over 100 years old and in the wrong place.

The first step in the reconstruction was to purchase the leased land to the north and west of the site and this was achieved for the sum of £20,000. An initial plan was then set down showing the boundaries, the main shops and the welding shop, which were too good to scrap. If any other building fitted in, so much the better. If not, then neither sentiment nor book value was to mar the planning or enthusiasm.

Material flow was drawn down and a new internal railway system planned. Layout of plant and machines, office planning and architecture were examined, also the human problems such as washing, changing and lavatory accommodation.

Throughout the planning and construction phases Whessoe planners kept in front of them specific aims to make the Works a good place to be in. One which would make Whessoe equal to the best firms in the world in terms of quality and competitiveness and not just to spend money on a grandiose scheme.

These aims and objectives were defined quite specifically as:

1. Production involves the handling of large tonnages of materials. Any new layout should ensure a smooth flow of materials and finished products with a minimum of handling.
2. Each shop to be efficiently laid out as to machining positions and floor space and to be properly located in relation to other shops. Each shop to be capable of receiving and handling materials from other shops or supply to them.
3. The works should be a pleasant place to work in, attention to be paid to heating, ventilation, lighting, colour and floors and to an orderly arrangement of roads, paths and yards and also to the design of buildings and gardens.
4. Better provision than before should be made for washing, changing and lavatories.
5. The design of a new office block, better positioned and with a layout that provided inter-relation of departments, so necessary to production efficiency.
6. It is hoped by good planning and architecture to build a Works which would not only be highly efficient but would also be a local

amenity and a beauty spot rather than an eyesore in an industrial neighbourhood.

A working party under the leadership of Wilf Stairmand the Works Engineer was set up to co-ordinate the planning and architects were engaged to design and detail the changes. The architects were Sir John Burnet, Tait and Partners who had been responsible for the British Museum, the Empire Exhibition in 1937 and Sydney Harbour Bridge, and now WHESSOE.

The first decision was to extend the main shops by adding bays on the east and west sides and by increasing the lengths of all the shops. This brought the whole of the production into one main shop group within which the various processes could be properly integrated.

The 100 year old buildings were to be demolished as well as the old press shop, the heating boiler and the compressor house, thus removing one of the main bottle-necks in the Works, leaving an unobstructed exit northwards from all five of the main shops.

The next problem tackled was the provision of a new gantry, which was to have a span of 100 feet and a length of 400 feet. It had to be placed at an angle to the fronts of the shops due to the narrowness of the site at that point. To conform to this angled gantry the south end of each shop was extended by varying lengths so that the gantry was equidistant from each shop entrance.

These extensions served to house the new template loft, personnel blocks, works offices and incoming material areas.

During this period all substantial incoming and outgoing loads travelled by rail and an improved rail layout took shape, entering the Works near Foundry Street and leaving the east side at about the centre of the site.

The location of the stockyard and gantry effectively divided the Works into two parts. The area between the gantry and Brinkburn Road was to provide space for a research building and for social requirements which included car parks, gardens and the bowling green. A new entrance onto Brinkburn Road also opened up the site at both east and south sides.

A further stage of reconstruction was the provision of better facilities for the comfort and well-being of the men on the shop floor. The thought and planning which went into that was the first real indication of a change in attitudes between management and labour. Credit for much of this attitude change was given, quite rightly I believe, to Mr. A G Grant the General Manager at that time and later to succeed Claude Spielman as Managing Director.

It was accepted that each man spent nearly nine hours a day at his work and was entitled to good facilities and working conditions during those hours. The things that made for pleasant working conditions were lighting, heating, shop layout and decoration and separate provision for clothing, washing and lavatory requirements. The appearance of the site as a whole had also to be a major consideration.

In endeavouring to give the site a pleasing appearance, designs for concrete and glass buildings were considered and rejected.

The decision finally being taken to use only enough glass to provide adequate lighting. It was too easy to use more glass than necessary to achieve a modern look and so get cold rooms and shops in the long northern winters. (That was not the policy adopted, however, when designing the later office blocks in 1960/70.)

The offices, all small buildings and the facings of all the workshops were to be built using yellow or sand coloured bricks the same as the existing canteen buildings, which was built in 1942.

The shop floors were all to be hard surfaced and marked to show walkways and areas for raw and finished materials. A standard colour scheme was adopted, cream was used for all inside steelwork, turquoise blue for overhead cranes, and blue for all machine tools. All outside steelwork was painted turquoise blue to contrast with the sand coloured brickwork.

All lighting was planned to give good general uniform illumination with a minimum of "black spots" thus minimising eye-strain and accidents. Safety at work became a much more prominent requirement.

Not a great deal of attention was given to accident prevention until the post-war years. Even then the men themselves tended to resist the use of ear defenders, safety goggles, gloves and barrier cream on the grounds that they restricted their movements. The more likely reason was that it was not seen to be manly to use them.

Heating and ventilation was also a new innovation for workshops and much credit has to be given to the management of the time for the thought and consideration that went into that aspect. All shops were fitted with gas heaters which were developed jointly by Whessoe engineers and Pools a local heating company. They were thought to be the most advanced shop heaters of that time.

The heaters drew in cool air from floor level, heated it and projected it at a height of 14 feet. This gave as near as possible a uniform air temperature in the large shops of about 60°F.

The system also provided for the intake and heating of fresh air from outside and for the discharge of surplus air at floor level. This effectively gave an "air change" process with, for example, the welding shop with its welding fumes, having its air changed every two hours. In all cases the volume of air per person exceeded that of a first class cinema.

The heaters were never actually as effective as hoped and in later years were supplemented with radiant gas heaters.

Nevertheless they were a major improvement on the old coke braziers.

The next facility that was most welcome to the majority of the workforce was the provision of personnel blocks to provide washing, lavatory and locker facilities.

With over 750 employees spread over 15 acres of shops and yards it was not easy to provide these particular facilities.

The final scheme entailed the building of three central personnel blocks, two for personnel in the main shops and stockyard and one for those working in the welding and pickling shops and on the Ring.

Each block was to be adequate for up to 320 men and included wash basins, toilets of modern design (good-bye "four-holer") two shower baths and a clothes locker and seat locker for each man.

The cloakrooms were to be heated in such a way that wet clothes hanging in lockers with perforated doors would dry in an hour or two.

It was hoped that these facilities would encourage men to wash and change at the end of the day and although it took some time it was the start of a new social regime with men going home in clean clothes and leaving their overalls and Whessoe dirt behind them.

The next but vital piece of planning was the design of a new office block. This was finally designed as a three storey, flat roofed Tee sectioned building between the existing canteen and the east boundary.

The internal arrangement of the offices was dominated by two considerations.

The drawing office had to be on the top floor so that it could have roof lights and the Personnel Department should adjoin the Works entrance on the ground floor to be closely in touch with the Wages Department and the Works Managers Department. (Most personnel problems start at the pay packet.)

It was then important that offices and departments should be in close touch with their opposite number. I understand that twenty- five different layouts were made before the optimum solution was reached.

Incidentally, one colour chosen for the internal décor was daffodil yellow, a dramatic change from the then conventional browns and creams, originally scoffed at but eventually found to be very cheerful and acceptable. The reconstruction plans were now complete and with the Bovis Company selected as the builder's work could go ahead on the building demolition and land levelling.

Building started with the new office block and this had been completed and inhabited during 1948. The old office block was demolished and the land prepared for the new gantry and stockyard in the same year. It took a further two years for the erection of the garage, Research and Development laboratories and test tower and a weigh-bridge and associated office.

The next stage was the construction of the extended frontages on the south end of the main shops. The balance of the original reconstruction plan took until 1954 to complete, the last stage being the completion of the third personnel block. The cost of the reconstruction was originally estimated at £500,000 but the final cost, due to additions and improvements, was closer to £1,000,000.

*Whessoe's new office block at Darlington, completed in 1948 as part of
the major works reconstruction.*

It should be appreciated that in order to determine the exact requirements of the reconstruction there had to be considerable discussions
with all levels of staff and labour. One of the most useful tools of
communication proved to be the "Forum" which was developed from
experiences gained, again in the war years.

During those years a Works Joint Production Committee comprising
management, foremen, and unions met to discuss and resolve production
problems. This committee fell into disuse shortly after the end of the
war. It was resurrected in 1947 when a joint meeting of representatives
from management, staff, trade unions and foremen was again set up.

The purpose of this body was to provide a means for the management
to make known and to obtain guidance on its plans, policies and development and for the employees to express specific recommendations for
improvements. This meeting proved to be a tremendous success and
from it was developed a properly constituted body to be called the
"Forum" which was officially inaugurated in February 1948.

Aerial view of the Darlington works near the end of the reconstruction project in 1952.

Twenty-three representatives from management and supervisory staff were appointed by the Company. A further twenty-one people representing the various departments throughout the offices and Works were elected by secret ballot. These included apprentices, female staff, general office staff and skilled and unskilled labour and they stood for one year periods.

The rules stipulated that the Managing Director (C.M. Spielman) would be permanent Chairman and the General Manager (A.G. Grant) Deputy Chairman.

The first official meeting was convened on the 10th May 1949. All staff and Works employees were welcome to attend the meetings as an audience. Many guest speakers were brought in to discuss many diverse subjects and was a great help in developing relations between management and staff/labour.

The Forum in fact heralded another real change in management attitude towards employees, by acknowledging that they had something useful to contribute to the development of the company and were worth listening to. The Forum continued as a very useful communication tool for over twenty years but was eventually disbanded by mutual agreement.

Direct communication suffered, I feel, as a result and only returned, although to a lesser extent, in 1989/1990 with the advent of Information Technology in its broader sense.

8

The Nineteen Fifties

Now that I was back in harness I concentrated on completing my apprenticeship and becoming a journeyman, that is a qualified tradesman on full pay. As I explained earlier as an Interrupted Apprentice my wages were subject to a 10 per cent reduction at source and at that time I was probably earning about £2.10s. a week after deductions.

During my absence a new peace-time product line had been introduced—Shell and Tube heat exchangers (although it is fair to say that one or two had been manufactured before the war). I was seconded to the exchanger squad as my first job making up a complement of six fitters under a chargehand—Dick Longstaff.

Dick himself had recently returned from the army where he had been a quartermaster-sergeant in the Middle East. He never lost his acquisitive abilities and our squad always managed to get the best equipment and, more importantly, the best piece-work prices for our work.

He eventually became shop convener for the Amalgamated Engineering Union (A.E.U.) and was responsible for many of the improvements in working conditions and pay conditions, including pensions and sick pay negotiations during the 1950s. Dick became my mentor and close friend for almost twenty years until he died at the age of 50 not long after his transition to the "staff".

The heat exchangers at this time were designed by the Lummus Company, an American design house with offices in London. Depending upon the complexity of the units, Whessoe was charged a fee of 2.5 per cent to 5 per cent of the exchanger selling price, for the design

Large heat exchanger tube bundle being assembled at Whessoe's Darlington works.

and detailed drawings which were transposed into working drawings in our own drawing office.

A heat exchanger was basically a boiler with a bundle of tubes fastened at each end by a tubeplate, which was then inserted into a steel fabricated barrel or shell and closed off with a fabricated or cast channel or return cover. These exchangers provided work for almost all of the inherent skills at Whessoe which made them an ideal manufacturing product line.

The shells and return covers were rolled from steel plate and welded using techniques developed during the war. The tubeplates were machined and drilled in the fitting and machine shops. A 30 inch diameter tubeplate could have up to 350 one inch diameter tube holes drilled to an accuracy of two thousandths of an inch. This is where the skills of the marker-off and driller came in.

I could probably write a separate book on heat exchangers alone as I was eventually connected with them for over twenty-five years, in various spheres of operation at Whessoe.

The phases of development are interesting though.

Starting with the Lummus Heat Exchanger we really needed only draughtsmen to draw and tradesmen to build them at that time, and in the early stages we were building only about five or six at any one time with a typical completion period for a complete exchanger of about twelve weeks.

One of the final stages of manufacture was the inspection and testing of the completed product. The tests were carried out using water at pressures of 100 p.s.i. to 300 p.s.i. with visual checks for leaks at tube ends and flange joint.

Critical inspection techniques had been developed during the war and initially we had one inspector allocated to the assembly and testing of exchangers. He was a time served tradesman who was promoted to foreman and then transferred to inspection during the war years and was "Works Staff"—the then elevated position between worker and office staff.

He worked Works hours and was paid a monthly salary generally in line with the average piece work earnings on the shop floor. Unlike a foreman, he had to tread a delicate line between supervisor and supervised. He worked closely with the fitters but had to criticize their work if wrong.

He also had to be seen to be doing a good job on behalf of the ultimate customer who sent their own inspectors for the final tests. In addition, of course, he also had to keep his eye on the main chance of ultimate promotion to office staff status, if he was so inclined.

The man I always remember was, for want of a better name, called Sidney. He was very proud of his position and always had aspirations to a more senior position on the staff. Towards that end he tended to emulate the visiting inspectors from London, who were chiefly ex-navy engineering officers at that time with cultured southern accents, somewhat different from the north-east dialect. Unfortunately he never quite got it right and was well remembered for a particular incident.

A visiting inspector asked him if he was sure that the material of a particular tubeplate was aluminium-bronze to which he replied, "Ho yes its alimillium cos I seed it writ on the drawring".

The visiting inspector had the manners to keep a straight face and not correct Sidney on his faulty grammar. Surprisingly we didn't either and Sid never realised he had said anything wrong, although for many years he was referred to by one and all as "seed it writ".

Heat exchanger orders developed rapidly over the next few years, until eventually Whessoe became one of the "big five" in U.K. heat exchanger manufacture. With orders obtained for over 100 exchangers at a time. It was necessary to increase the squads and double and treble shift activities.

To get to this position it became necessary to develop our own designs. The Research and Development department under Francombe and Puttick set out to produce thermal designs from client's specifications and then, of course, came full mechanical designs.

Eventually a chemical engineer, called Saunders, was allotted the task of setting-up a department for the development of viable and competitive thermal and mechanical designs for all types of exchangers. So was formed the Whessoe Heat Exchanger Department under the leadership of E.A.D. Saunders, affectionately known as Eads or Ted.

Ted Saunders retired from Whessoe after thirty year's service during which he gained an international reputation as one of the foremost engineers in the thermal design of heat exchanger's with the authorship of several papers and books to his credit. I believe he is still called upon to lecture at overseas venues.

Going back to 1948, I stayed on heat exchangers for nearly two years but on occasion some of us were moved to help out on other products, which gave us a greater interest.

In June 1950 I was asked, or rather told, to go to site to expand some gas condenser tubes in units that had been designed and built by Whessoe for Appleby Frodingham Steel Co. at Scunthorpe.

Although Whessoe had been involved in site construction for most of its history it was an activity almost totally divorced from the Darlington Works. The Erection department had their own staff and labour force and in fact were a separate Division of Whessoe Engineering. The only direct contact I had was in 1943 when I served as an office boy for Dick Parker. Once in the Works I had lost all interest in sites.

One had to be an individual with a particular attitude of mind to work away from home for many months at a time. I was pretty much of a home boy despite my years in the forces but, more particularly, as I was courting a certain young redhead in the Accounts Department at that time.

During my National Service my old friend Ted Harland had retired and had been replaced by Harold Johnson a foreman of considerable experience, most of it on construction sites across the world. It was he who insisted that I went to site and would not brook any argument—it was a great life for a single man, as far as he was concerned.

I was told that they wanted someone to expand by hand the ends of about 200 six inch diameter tubes into the top and bottom tube-plates of two vertical condensers—it would take only ten days!

I was seconded to the Erection Department for the duration of the work and given a railway warrant and £1 expenses to get to site by public transport.

In those days a lodging allowance of fifteen shillings (75p) a week was provided and for that one could get full board, of a sort.

There was a Site Services Manager on the steelworks whose job it was to secure accommodation for all contractor's employees as well as their own labour. Scunthorpe was a real boom town after the war, with all the reconstruction work going on. The town was flooded with immigrant labour and good lodgings were hard to come by.

I remember being sent to an address, behind a veterinary surgeon's shop, that already had eight other lodgers. Although we slept separately we all shared the same bath and toilet facilities. Despite this the place was clean and the food reasonable.

The first morning I took a bus to site for 8.00 a.m. and the foreman introduced me to the job. This was the first let down—not only were there double the number of tubes to expand but one of the condensers hadn't even been built yet. There was no way I was going to be finished in ten days.

The condensers were steel rectangular boxes 30 ft. × 10 ft. × 60 ft. high with large diameter tubes expanded into top and bottom tubeplates. The sides of the condenser rose five feet above the top tubeplate and the bottom plate was in an enclosed compartment three feet high.

Each tube had to be man-handled with a rope sling and then lowered onto a jack in the bottom compartment. The top end was then expanded and the jack moved to the next hole and so on.

Expanding the top tubes was a back aching job but was even worse in the bottom chamber. It was too low to stand or even squat so one had to sit and pull on the expander and consequently slide along the steel bottom plate which, as you can imagine, generated considerable soreness after a few hundred tube ends. It got so bad that the only way I could continue was to get a loan of 7s. 6d. from the site foreman and buy a motor-cycle pillion cushion and strap this under me (I had to pay the 7s. 6d. back incidentally).

This so called ten day job actually took twelve weeks and about half way through this period I started to have problems with my lodgings. We all noticed eventually that we got very little meat with our meals, our lunch-time sandwiches always contained lettuce and tomato. We then realized that the landlady was selling our meat coupons to the veterinary surgeon at the front who went home every week with about two pounds of our bacon under his arm.

Despite many protestations it went on for some time until it came to a head when the Whessoe administration faltered and they forgot to send my lodging allowance and I was unable to pay my rent.

The landlady reported me to the Site Manager responsible for accommodation and I was hauled in front of him. After listening to my explanation and contacting Whessoe on my behalf, but also after corroborating my comments on the conditions at the lodgings, the place was struck off their approved list and I was offered new accommodation.

This turned out to be a palace in comparison. It was the home of a young couple with a small baby, the place was exceptionally clean and the food excellent.

It was almost two weeks before I met the husband, as he was on night shift at the steel mills. But one day I noticed a photograph on the wall, of an R.A.F. squadron of recruits and right in the front was a corporal with a very familiar face. This was one of the many coincidences I mentioned early in the book. It turned out to be Corporal Carpenter of Greenham Common fame. I'd finished up, four years after my square bashing, in his house.

ONE OF WHESSOE'S FASTEST WORKERS.

The author's wedding announcement in the Whessoe magazine 1950, typical of those produced by the talented Les Blakeborough.

Eventually the condenser contract came to a close and I was able to return to Darlington, my not too happy period with site construction at an end and swearing that I would never work away again. Little did I know.

My return was quite timely as I was due to get married to the redhead from Accounts one month later.

During this period I still had 10 per cent deducted from my wages as an Interrupted Apprentice but the end of the job saw the completion of my apprenticeship. I was now able to earn a skilled tradesman's wage of £5 a week.

About this time in 1950, Whessoe had taken up a licence to manufacture Venting and Measuring equipment for petroleum product storage tanks from an American company Shand & Jurs in California. Initially these were relatively small items in aluminium and plastic materials, formed, machined and assembled from Shand & Jurs drawings.

It was a product line that fitted into the existing machining and fitting shop techniques, using equipment that had been developed during the war.

I was transferred to Shand & Jurs to help Bob Earle, an ex- railway fitter, as the work load started to increase. For some months we worked together to help develop manufacturing and testing methods with people from the drawing and engineering departments, my first real direct contact with the "staff". Eventually I was involved solely in the development, trials and testing of new and additional items covering the whole range of fitting and machining skills.

This product line was the forerunner of the light engineering side of Whessoe which is now recognised world wide as Whessoe Systems & Controls Ltd. and has become the linchpin of the Whessoe Group.

I stayed on Shand & Jurs for almost ten years as the chargehand fitter over a squad of twenty fitters and apprentices. During that period I learned a lot more about people and attitudes and relationships between Staff and Works which began to change, literally and also in my own mind as I matured and began to see the "other side's" point of view on many matters.

The newer and younger draughtsmen and designers, brought in to develop new fittings, had a more modern attitude. Conversation was generally on a first name basis, which at that time was a major breakthrough.

I do remember, however, one particular instance, which is a good example of the "them and us" syndrome that still prevailed.

As a chargehand of probably one of the largest working squads in the Company I became the contact between the manufacturing side and the design and management teams and consequently struck up a good working relationship with several engineers. On this particular day I had occasion to go over to the offices to check a particular feature and the engineer in question, who incidentally was on general staff and not particularly senior at that time, was not available. I asked one of his colleagues, with whom he shared his office, if R**** was about and was told that he would be most annoyed at me referring to him by his first name and I should in future ask for Mr.******.

Rather than react aggressively to this pettiness I asked that Mr. ****** be informed that Mr. Hockin would like to discuss a design problem with him and left it at that. The only real satisfaction I eventually got from that encounter was that over ensuing years I was to see my own career taking me past that particular gentleman, in terms of position and status in the Company.

Fortunately these occurrences were becoming more rare, with Staff and Works working together more as members of a team than opponents, although it did in fact take many years to produce more harmonious attitudes on both sides.

I continued as a chargehand fitter for a period of about ten years and during that time found that the work necessitated several periods of site work despite my protestations and reluctance to go.

Shand & Jurs were expanding fairly rapidly and a lot of fittings were being sold to refineries throughout the country. There was a need to install and modify equipment on-site and who better to do that than the people who made them and had the knowledge of their intricacies, but more importantly, held the right union card for working on the sites. The engineering industry at that time was, of course, completely "closed shop".

These trips of two to three weeks duration were still never to my liking but became a necessity. Conditions were somewhat better than before, with even the opportunity to stay in hotels on occasion, albeit the more seedy ones.

The situation that had the most significant affect on my future working life was brought about by an offer from the shop foreman for me to go on a two-day trip to Grangemouth Chemical Works with an engineer from the offices to witness the official handover to B.P. of a tank installation fitted with Shand & Jurs fittings.

My immediate reaction was to reject the offer as I had had enough of Whessoe site work by this time.

I was eventually persuaded to go with the knowledge that I would be wearing my good suit (the only one at that time) and would be staying in a top class hotel at Stirling. And it was, after all, only for two days, travel on the Thursday and return on the Friday and be driven by the engineer. It was seen as a form of reward for past work.

The journey in those days took about five hours by road. During that time the engineer, who was evidently most disgruntled at having to travel with a workman, even in his best suit, refused to indulge in any conversation for the whole of the journey.

We booked into separate rooms at the Golden Lion hotel in Stirling and arranged to meet in the dining room at 7.30 p.m. for dinner.

The problem I encountered was that he had arrived early in the restaurant and had ordered his own meal from the *à la carte* menu, written entirely in French without translation. I didn't understand a word and my colleague felt it beneath him to help me, so I had to rely on the waiter to translate for me, which was somewhat embarrassing.

This account will be showing the reader that there were still significant pockets of snobbishness, taken to the extreme, which didn't bode well for future working relationships. The most significant part of this tale, however, was to follow.

On the Friday morning having presented ourselves at the site offices for the handover. We went to the new pump house where there was an array of hand operated pumps used for opening and closing the L.P.G. valves on six high pressure spheres, to be told that none of them worked. The hydraulic lines had been tested with water instead of oil with subsequent corrosion and blockage of the valve filters. They had been rejected by B.P. who were insisting on immediate replacements.

My engineer friend went off to telephone head office to advise them of the situation. He came back with the instructions that I was to stop over to dismantle all the valves and pumps, clean them and replace and test them ready for operation on Monday morning. In anticipation of my refusal he had been given instructions that I was to be dismissed if I did refuse, which in hindsight of course wouldn't have got the job done by Monday. But it was sufficient of a threat to cause me concern in view of the fact that we had by this time a young baby to support.

We debated the situation for some time quite heatedly, although the outcome was inevitable, particularly as I didn't have any money for my return train fare and my friend refused to give me a lift as he was going off on holiday and had no intention of staying with me.

The next problem was where would I stay and how did I get about without transport. The answer was quite simple, book me into a seaman's hostel a mile from the site entrance and I could walk to work. The hostel cost 7s. 6d. per night for a room with an iron bed, no floor covering, a bedside cupboard with a Gideon Bible and a nail in the wall to hang my coat.

The washing facilities were a communal stone trough with cold water only. But the breakfast was marvellous. Thick slices of fried bread with sausage and bacon and a mug of tea all to be shared with fellow vagrants, who in some cases were better company than the engineer.

Helped by B.P works staff, I worked Friday night, all day Saturday and finished the job at 11.00 a.m. on Sunday morning and then took stock.

It was Sunday in Scotland and in 1955 everything closed on Sunday. I had no working clothes with me and my best and only suit was stained and marked with hydraulic oil, I hadn't had a shave and I had only £3 left, from the £5 the engineer had graciously given me for my train fare home. Even worse, trains to Darlington on a Sunday didn't stop at Stirling so I had to get to Edinburgh somehow to catch the only train at 3.00 p.m. which meant hitch hiking.

Fortunately this was not a problem. Although I must have looked somewhat dishevelled, eventually walking down Princes Street in Edinburgh on a Sunday afternoon with two days growth, a dirty, oil stained suit and the soles of both shoes flapping, as the hydraulic oil had rotted the stitches. *But at least I got home with the dubious satisfaction of knowing that another job had been successfully completed for Whessoe. My friend the engineer had managed to get away for his holiday without a problem and I was back in the bosom of my family ready to start work again at 7.30 a.m. next morning. More, significantly, I knew that this was definitely the last job I was going away on for Whessoe!!!*

Incidentally, in the then true generous style of that time, Whessoe reimbursed me to the tune of 5s. to have my suit cleaned. But the damaged shoes were considered to be fair wear and tear and, in any case, I was being paid for all the overtime hours I had worked over the week-end. As I said earlier, it was this particular episode that made me take stock of my life and come to some decisions on my future.

At this time I was 28 years old, a chargehand fitter, which incidentally paid me a total income of £600 per year. This included an extra 10s. a week for supervising twenty-three other fitters, arranging their work load, calculating and negotiating the piece-work rates as well as ensuring that I did sufficient work to earn my own share of the piece-work earnings.

I had no formal education and of course no qualifications at all. Not a lot to go on! It seemed at the time though that the grass was much greener on the staff side of the street and that was where I should be looking.

After one or two tentative enquiries it soon became apparent that there was not going to be any real opportunity for transfer without some form of engineering qualification.

The only previous opportunities had been towards the end of the war when people like Ray Rocket, Bill Moore and Bob Young had completed their apprenticeships and had been given opportunities in the Estimating Office after achieving at least O.N.C. standards at night-school.

Since leaving the forces in 1948 I had given little thought to education, concentrating mainly on earning a living and supporting a young family. This obviously had to change and after a lot of thought and discussion with my wife I finally enrolled for night school in September 1956 with the object of obtaining at least the O.N.C. in mechanical engineering.

This was a bigger decision than it sounds. I was 28 years old, married with a young child, faced with three nights a week of schooling, starting right back in the first year syllabus in a class of 16 year olds. Quite a blow to my pride. It also meant a reduction in my earning power as our weekly wage was bolstered by a regular two nights' overtime which of course had to be forgone.

Having made the decision, however, we persevered and the first year was probably the most difficult time for me, as getting back into the swing of learning after fourteen years was very difficult. Whereas the 16 year olds appeared to absorb the lessons without any difficulty I had to go home each night and do the whole lesson again before it began to sink in. It was even worse on occasion when I found I was older than the lecturer. The one advantage I had was that now I wanted to learn, which was a much needed incentive.

During this period, apart from the introduction of heat exchangers and Shand & Jurs fittings into the scheme of things for Whessoe, other product lines were being considered. The Research and Development department was in its infancy but was managed and staffed by some very able people.

It functioned very much as the title suggested with one area researching new ways of producing new products and the other area physically developing production methods and inspection and testing techniques.

With welding now an established process, considerable effort was put into the development of welding procedures and, of course, the metallurgical aspects of the process.

In 1945 a new standard lap-welded tank was introduced, replacing the riveted technique and it was hoped it would remain a standard for many years. However, by 1950 a new butt-welded design was introduced, which involved larger and thicker steel plates and a great unsolved question of plate edge bevelling.

The existing mechanical planing machines were in many cases too small and we turned to flame-burning, although again the existing equipment was not accurate enough and the R. & D. department were having to develop new equipment which, really, one would have expected to have been done by the equipment suppliers. To keep ahead of the field, however, Whessoe invested heavily in the welding process and all of its associated equipment.

Welding development at Whessoe warrants a book of its own but sufficient to say that over the ensuing years Whessoe were in the forefront of all welding techniques. This included, manual metal arc, automatic and semi-automatic T.I.G., M.I.G., CO_2-Finewire, electroslag, tube end welding and fully computerised orbital welding in many grades of carbon steel and alloys in thicknesses from 3mm to 250mm.

Of course, although welding was one of R.& D.'s greatest involvements, it was also initially involved in the development of gas-plant equipment, insulation, plastics, stress analysis, strain gauge testing, tank gauging equipment, electric precipitate and electro-detarrers for gas works and played a vital role in the success of Whessoe as a heavy engineering specialist company.

During the 1950s Craft Apprentice Training became a much more formal matter and considerably more thought was given to the abrupt transition from school to work. Like me, most boys only had the vaguest idea of what work really meant and of the responsibilities they accepted for themselves on the day that they did start work. Works visits were, therefore, encouraged before the pupils left school so that they would have at least some idea of the new environment and conditions that they were committing themselves to.

The major part of apprenticeship training was still done by the craftsmen with whom they worked. It was recognised that any training scheme would fail if the craftsmen were not encouraged to pass on their knowledge of the trade.

With modern methods of training and education apprentices would have much greater opportunities than their predecessors, although it was also accepted that the modern machine age was a mixed blessing in that it eliminated in many cases full practise of hand tools. With this philosophy Whessoe introduced one of the first Apprentice Training Schools in the North-East, which gave youngsters theoretical training and basic hand tool usage in the first year. It was followed by more advanced training on the shop floor interspersed with more theoretical engineering at night school and eventually day school.

The first few months were also a golden opportunity to assess individual apprentices mental and physical capabilities and by mutual agreement direct a boy to the trade to which he was most suited, rather than just follow in his father's footsteps, as had usually happened in the past.

Whessoe at that time had a strong need for new blood in the Works mainly in the boilersmith trades, to cope with the predominance of tankage and construction work being sought. But, despite this need, Whessoe took what was seen to be a very forward looking attitude and agreed that it would be wrong to train apprentices purely for Whessoe's own selfish needs and that they would be trained with a view to getting the best results, not only for the firm but for the community as a whole.

To ensure this happened a Youth Advisory Panel was set up made up of Management, Personnel, Works Staff and Shop floor represent-atives. This Panel had the closest possible contact with Youth Employment Officers, Education Authorities and various School Headmasters in the area.

The Ability screening in the first year was followed up throughout the five year training period and as particular educational capabilities were developed suitable apprentices were allowed to transfer to Higher Educational classes with a view to developing their careers into Engin-eering drawing, design and special management areas.

It was acknowledged throughout the Heavy Engineering Industry that by becoming a recognized apprentice under the Whessoe scheme he was assured of a sound practical and theoretical training and there were always opportunities open throughout the world for such men.

You will note that reference has always been made to boys with regard to engineering apprentices and it must be said that little thought was given to the employment of girls in craft training and indeed it is doubtful whether any were interested at that time.

Eventually, however, in the 1970s one or two girls came into the scheme but never stayed long on the shop floor.

Despite the success of such apprentice training schemes, in the 1980s the market forces which indicated the decline in Heavy engineering requirements throughout the country and indeed the world brought about a gradual reduction in apprentice acceptance. Eventually the school, along with many others throughout the country, was closed with the loss of a valuable source of training for the Engineering Industry.

This loss is being even more dramatized today with an ageing work-force and no formally trained back-up and consequently a sad dearth of such skills within the industry.

This is finally being acknowledged, in that currently in the 1990s much more emphasis is being placed on the co-operation between qualified engineers and schools in an attempt to stem the decline in recruitment into the engineering industry.

In an earlier reference to the Works layout, the Ring and the Pickler were briefly mentioned and during 1954 dramatic development of both these areas was completed.

If one mentions the Ring most people will think of boxing or the circus. But mention the Ring to a man who knows Whessoe and he will automatically call to mind stacks of steel plates, bundles of sections, piles of dished ends, partly fabricated work of all descriptions, mobile cranes, platers, welders, burners, helpers etc. Indeed all the fun of a construction engineering circus was contained in a 230 feet diameter concrete area ringed by rail tracks, known as the Erecting Yard at Whessoe.

For many years the Ring had been the hub of activity for sorting, marking, bundling and the packing of materials for shipment. It was

Final stages in the reconstruction of the 'Ring'.

there also that the trial erection of fabricated plate and section work had been done.

In the summer of 1954, when the Works closed for the annual two weeks' holiday, a reconstruction crew moved in to begin the work that would change for ever the face of the Ring. Within the two weeks the whole area was excavated. Ducting for power lines, water and air was laid. Old rail tracks were taken up and the whole area concreted to merge with the surrounding land.

The old steam cranes had been dispensed with and rubber tyred mobile cranes and trailers were used to move materials without the restriction of rail tracks. During the reconstruction work many old landmarks had disappeared and although the area no longer bore any resemblance to its name Whessoe men will always have warm memories of that part of Whessoe called "THE RING".

Again the term "Pickling" conjures up many varied descriptions. In the steel fabrication business the pickling process had been a necessary requirement for many decades. It was generally accepted that if steel was to be preserved by painting then all traces of mill-scale, rust and grease must be removed first.

When steel leaves the rolling mill it is covered with a layer of mill-scale consisting of iron-oxides which form a hard and brittle layer adhering to the metal. The mill-scale, however, contains microscopic cracks through which moisture will penetrate causing rusting of the steel and lifting of the scale, together with any paint films which have been applied.

If structures can be left unpainted and exposed to the weather for six months to two years, rusting will ensure the lifting of the mill-scale. This is known as weathering and the suitability of the surface is determined by the effectiveness of the necessary scraping and wire-brushing. Another method is to sand blast the surface to remove the scale and rust. This is an effective method but the cost is prohibitive for large steel plates.

The usual method of pre-treatment is by acid pickling. Sulphuric and hydrochloric acids were originally used but caused their own problems of corrosion if all traces were not removed by thorough washing.

This problem was overcome by using phosphoric acid which left a rust resisting film of iron sulphate on the metal. Phosphoric acid was much easier to handle than other acids and caused less trouble with spray from the baths.

The Shell Petroleum Co. Limited and Whessoe jointly developed a process of sulphuric/phosphoric acid pickling which proved to be the most effective and economic to operate.

Three baths were needed to carry out the process. The first contained a 5 per cent solution of sulphuric acid heated to 65°C and steel was immersed in this for fifteen to thirty minutes. After pickling, the plates were drained over the bath and then transferred to the second bath containing hot water at 60°C and dipped twice. The third stage was to immerse the plates in the third tank containing a 2 per cent solution of phosphoric acid and 0.5 per cent iron for five minutes.

The plates were finally laid down and allowed to dry after rinsing which left a phosphate coating. They were then given a coat of priming paint.

The old existing pickling facility had been in use for years and was dark, dismal and fume filled. In line with Whessoe's plans for providing

'Men at Work' in the new Pickling Shop, a much improved environment in 1954.

larger more modern facilities it was decided to demolish the old pickling shop and build a new one in a more suitable place.

Dismantling the old shop was no problem. Excavating the land to achieve new levels required the digging up and disposal of 23,000 cubic yards of earth weighing more that 22,000 tons. Eventually 5,000 lorry loads were transported to the South Park in the west end of Darlington and were used to fill in the old boating lake and part of the river Skerne was re-routed in a straight line. The lake area was re-defined as a miniature golf course and is still in use today.

The old pickler land proved to be extremely fertile in concrete blocks and many of them weighing anything from ten to twenty tons were found 4 feet below the surface. One of the old Whessoe theories, that the old foremen were pickled and buried there proved, however, to be untrue.

It seemed that reconstruction would never finish, as fast as one new facility was completed another one was planned and installed.

In the six years from 1954 to 1959 a new stress relieving furnace was built at the end of the welding shop at the north end of the site. A Shadow marking facility for the edge marking of sphere plates was designed and built, along with a sphere plate edge burning facility which burned edge preparations on pre- pressed sphere plates. This was a large pendulum operated piece of equipment, designed by the R. & D. department and subsequently patented.

A large new welding shop was built with its own Isotope building for the examination of welded seams up to 150mm thickness.

In 1956 a new 4,500 ton ram press with its own plate furnace and furnace charging equipment was purchased and erected in the new press shop. In 1957 a third floor extension was erected on the north

The pendulum edge burning machine was designed, patented and built by Whessoe engineers to enable pre-formed heavy plate to be cut to exact radii complete with edge preparation for welding. The plates were marked off by light projection methods.

end of the offices and was used to house the ever expanding Construction Division and then later the Special Projects Group.

Plans were developed for a massive new pressure vessel welding
shop and the first earth was moved at the end of 1959.

In the years immediately after the war the industry had an extensive
catching-up period. During the war years there had been very little
building of tanks, gas plant or chemical plant other than those required
for the immediate war needs and after 1945 despite steel rationing
Whessoe's own order books were full when those lost years had to be
made up.

The nationalization of the gas industry by the Labour Government
led to the construction of new gas-works and gas-making plant and the
decision by the oil companies to refine oil in Britain led to the vast
refinery programme at Stanlow, Shell Haven, Fawley and elsewhere as

*The Fielding and Pratt 4,500 ton ram press capable of hot pressing
steel plate up to 12" thick.*

well as other demands made by the Korean war. All of this meant that for nearly ten years, up to the mid fifties, Whessoe and its competitors had full order books, often for more than a year ahead.

The reconstruction of the Works proved invaluable in meeting the demands for tanks, spheres, pressure vessels, heat exchangers and gas plant equipment. The executive management deserved praise for their forethought. In particular, A.G. Grant who had taken over as Managing Director following the retirement of C.M. Spielman in 1954 after thirty-one years with Whessoe, nineteen of those as M.D.

To keep ahead of the market it was vital that Whessoe continued to invest in new developments, both in design and manufacturing methods. It was vital, too, that there was an even closer relationship between management and the work force to ensure that all activities were carried out in an efficient and profitable manner.

It was about this time that the use of Method Study, Motion Study and Work Measurement was mooted during one of the Forum meetings, which of course immediately set the Union representatives worrying about clamp down procedures on shop floor labour and a restriction in their earning power despite assurances from management that any studies would encompass all areas of staff and works.

There was no doubt that Time and Motion studies occupied the minds of many so-called experts and specialists. Most of the research had been done in the United States and all the recognized text books and reference books had been written by Americans and apparently related to factory activities only.

Unions at this time, which had seen the strength of their negotiating power and the earnings of the labour force grow tremendously throughout the country in the post-war years, quite naturally objected to any scheme which controlled labour only and made no attempt to restrain and monitor the activities of engineers and administrative staff who equally could have an adverse effect on efficiency and productivity.

It was acknowledged by the management that they could not expect results overnight from these schemes. Lengthy and detailed investigations would have to take place before serious consideration could be given to their overall use.

The full system was never actually introduced into Whessoe as it was finally agreed that the heavy engineering processes did not lend themselves to such control. But, the use of Method Study techniques as opposed to Time and Motion studies did bring about significant saving in time used in material movement and flow of work throughout its shop floor travels. The control of piece-work payments was also reviewed which meant that estimators had a more accurate forecast of job costs and therefore an opportunity to put in keener prices in the growing competitive market.

In spite of this competitive situation Whessoe continued to attract new orders, particularly from the Petroleum industry. Tank orders were flowing in steadily. Spheres and pressure vessels were becoming more and more ambitious in size, thickness and quality of steel. The heat exchanger demand was brisk and gas plant too was in a healthy state.

The outside erection department was particularly active with over one hundred sites operative in one year in such places as Nigeria, the Gold Coast, Sierra Leone and Cyprus. In 1956 Whessoe were erecting one complete storage tank per day, an excellent record.

There was a limiting factor however to this substantial workload. The British steel industry was having great difficulty producing the amount of steel required. Even though by 1957 it had increased its production by one million tons over that of the previous year the total output was still running probably one million tons short of the demand. In spite of imports from the U.S.A and the Continent steel was still rationed and fabricators were in the position of having to turn down orders or delay them awaiting steel allocations.

It was estimated that Whessoe could have increased its tankage order book by as much as 50 per cent had the steel been available. This situation continued until 1961 when new steel plate mills came into operation.

With this high demand for storage tanks, particularly in the petroleum field, one area of activity to grow and flourish was the Shand & Jurs tank fittings operation.

Members of the Research department had completed a long series of investigations into the operational losses through evaporation of petrol at storage installations. The results provided a basis for the economic assessment of the evaporation saving devices made under the Shand & Jurs licence and the work seemed important enough to be published and made available to industry at large. The publication excited great interest and orders flooded in for both land and marine based breathing and gauging equipment.

By 1957 Whessoe were selling equipment all over the world and had met and matched the American licensers' prices. The increased demand created a need for an additional production area to be built in the Works.

Moreover the S. & J. expansion was partly in the form of sales to the continent where the effects of the European Free Trade Association (EFTA) were important. France had virtually closed its doors to imports so arrangements were being explored for the manufacture of S. & J. fittings in France.

Also at this time Whessoe were negotiating the purchase of some British Railway land adjacent to the boundary fence, running from Brinkburn Road to the Stooperdale engine dismantling shops. In 1959 a new S. & J. building for storage and assembly was erected on this land, releasing the existing Works area for the expansion of heat exchanger production.

Another unique product developed at Whessoe during the 1950s was the design, manufacture and construction on site of Wind Tunnels for the Royal Aircraft Establishment at Bedford. Whessoe began work at Bedford as far back as 1947 carrying out various test assemblies for the R.A.E.

The first significant work was the building of a 3 ft. × 3 ft. square wind tunnel designed to test aircraft models at speeds as high as Mach 2, about 1,550 m.p.h. To maintain the desired operating temperatures during tests, coolers were built into the circuit and the tunnel itself was designed to operate at pressures of 15 p.s.i.g. or near vacuum.

Some sections of the tunnel were small enough to be fabricated in the Works but the larger sections had to be welded up on site. (The whole tunnel had an assembled length of 150 feet.) High quality welding was a must and each welder was periodically tested on site.

The second major project was a Vertical Spinning Tunnel which was very different from the horizontal 3 ft. × 3 ft. tunnel.

The vertical tunnel was designed to test the behaviour of free flying models and to study methods of recovery from spin. The speed of the air being much lower than the other unit at about 80 m.p.h.

The air was circulated by a fan at the top of a 15 feet diameter working section and returned through a concentric diffuser outside the working section and the diffuser operated at pressure of about 45 p.s.i.g. The complete tunnel weighed 1,200 tons and was almost entirely site built and had to be absolutely vertical.

Very close working tolerances were imposed and achieved.

The third and most exciting project was an 8 ft. × 8 ft. High Speed Tunnel, designed to test model aircraft at speeds up to Mach 2.7, about 2,050 m.p.h. It was essentially a pressure vessel, the largest in Europe, forming a closed circuit with four rectangular corners.

Five thousand tons of steel were used in its construction and in view of the tunnel's size special methods had to be used to construct it. The various sections of the tunnel each weighing 120 tons were fabricated in a vertical position and then lifted into position using a 200 feet high crane.

As with the 3 ft. × 3 ft. tunnel the air flowing round the tunnel had to be cooled. A special cooler, 47 feet diameter was therefore included in the tunnel's structure and this was where the experiences of heat exchanger manufacture came in.

The cooler contained 58,000 tubes with a total length of 180 miles. The tubeplates and baffle plates for this cooler were made from plates welded together in the horizontal plane with all the holes being drilled using radial drilling machines and jigs to accurately locate the holes.

As in the case of other tunnels exacting work was carried out on internal fairings to produce the required air flow, particularly at the entry to the working section. Carefully planned construction and welding achieved a high degree of accuracy and smooth contours free from waves or irregularities at the welded joints.

Finally, to test the soundness of the shell of the tunnel, it was hydraulically tested to 1.5 times the working pressure. This was done

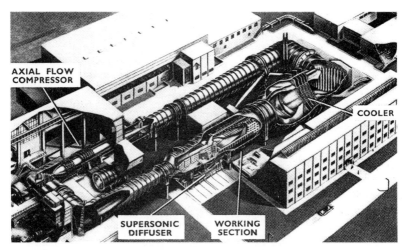

The 8' by 8' high speed wind tunnel, designed to test models at up to 2,050 m.p.h. Made from 5,000 tons of steel, it was the largest pressure vessel of its kind in Europe.

in three sections, the largest of which requiring 2.25 million gallons of water to fill it.

The overall size of the High Speed Tunnel and the Vertical Spinning Tunnel can be judged from the photographs.

The High Speed Tunnel project was valued at £30 million (a tremendous sum at that time) and the pressure vessel portion, of which Whessoe made the largest contribution, cost £11 million.

The Tunnel was officially opened and went operational in June 1957.

This historical account is attempting, amongst other things, to show the advancements and changes made over the years to the way Whessoe was managed and the way it adapted to the change in demand for different products.

Counting the war years there had been virtually seven periods of change and adaptation in the history of Whessoe, with the main core of business and the company's reputation being built upon the design and manufacture of gas plant, storage tanks, pressure vessels and heat exchangers.

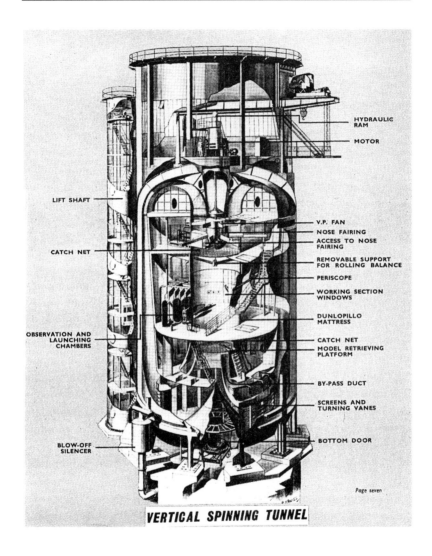

VERTICAL SPINNING TUNNEL

This vertical spinning tunnel for the aerodynamic testing of free flying models was designed and constructed by Whessoe's special projects division. Compare size with men on the 2nd and 4th levels.

The cooler for the high speed tunnel was 47 ft. diameter, containing over 50,000 tubes with a total length of 180 miles.

By the early 1950s, however, another new product line entered the order books which had a very significant impact on the future development of the company—NUCLEAR POWER. This is seen to be the eighth period of change in the history of Whessoe Heavy Engineering Ltd. and was to last for more than thirty years.

Before, during, and after the Second World War the use of atomic power as an energy source was being investigated. The development of the atomic bomb in 1945 expedited the research.

So much so that by 1949/1950 the harnessing of the nuclear chain reaction to provide a power source for peaceful use was well established.

The British Government had prepared a provisional programme which covered a ten year period and gave an indication of the probable development.

The first demonstration of the development of nuclear power for peaceful purposes was the building of Britain's first experimental nuclear power station at Calder Hall in Cumberland. This station was designed for both military plutonium production and power production purposes and was the first of its kind in the country and possibly the first of any magnitude in the world. The only other major existing British nuclear reactor being that at Windscale which was built by the A.E.A. in 1947 for purely military purposes and had two air-cooled piles for plutonium production. It operated until 1957 when it was destroyed by fire and sealed off.

The basic concept was produced by the United Kingdom Atomic Energy Authority (U.K.A.E.A) and was based on the generation of steam using gas-cooled graphite-moderated thermal reactors using as fuel, natural uranium or slightly enriched uranium.

To remove heat from the nuclear fuel rods the CO_2 coolant had to be circulated at the highest possible pressure. This called for very high integrity, thick wall pressure vessels, an area that Whessoe had excelled in with the Wind Tunnel work and the manufacture of reactor vessels for the petroleum and chemical industries.

Whessoe were called upon to collaborate in the design of these pressure vessels which had to deal with not only pressure stresses but the additional problems of thermal expansion and nuclear radiation effects. They had, of course, to remain sound indefinitely.

Reactors had to be built on the assumption that they could not be entered after start-up. Any information as to what was going on inside them could only be obtained from instruments and from removable samples of material which were exposed to the reactor environment which included high doses of radiation.

The design and manufacture of Calder Hall "A" which had two reactors introduced many firsts.

The foundations and the massive reinforced concrete structure or biological screen was a major civils project never attempted before.

The pressure vessels which were each 36 ft. diameter × 70 ft. high and made from 2 in. thick steel plate were constructed inside the concrete structure and stress relieved to minimise inherent stresses. It was the first time such vessels had been stress relieved by electrical means in the country and at that time were the biggest vessels to be stress relieved in the world.

Calder hall 'A' was completed, commissioned and officially opened by Her Majesty Queen Elizabeth on the 17th October 1956 after a twenty-seven months build period.

Prior to this completion, Whessoe in 1955 were awarded the contract for Calder Hall 'B', a further two reactor vessels.

It was acknowledged that the Calder Hall reactor vessels were the most important pressure vessels ever built. Without them Calder could not have happened and without Whessoe's developing experience the first forward step in the use of nuclear power for peaceful purposes would have been a much smaller one.

By 1955 another nuclear power station had been designed and Whessoe were awarded the contract for four reactor vessels for the Chapel Cross power station at Annan, Dumfriesshire. This was the first in Scotland and only the fourth in the world.

The design was the same as Calder hall, the only difference being in the layout. Chapel Cross reactors were built in-line, allowing for a single turbine house to serve all four reactors.

The station was designed to put 135 MW of electricity into the national grid plus the provision of plutonium for military purposes.

Irradiated elements (spent fuel), were stored safely in a "cooling pond" before being sent 70 miles by road to the plutonium factory at Windscale. Calder was so near to Windscale that a cooling pond was not necessary. The radio-active material, $1\frac{1}{4}$ tons at a time, would be transported in 40 ton, virtually undamageable lead lined, steel containers called flasks. (Whessoe were still making versions of these flasks under separate contract as late as 1990.)

The military reactors and the original dual purpose reactors at Windscale, Calder and Chapel Cross were researched, designed and built by the Atomic Energy Authority (A.E.A.) with the steel pressure retaining components being supplied by fabricators such as Whessoe, through the Ministry of Supply.

In 1954 the decision was taken to build a series of nuclear power stations for civil purposes only. Several private sector consortia were asked to tender for the complete design, construction and commissioning of these stations, assisted and funded by the United Kingdom Atomic Energy Authority (U.K.A.E.).

Whessoe then became a member of the new Nuclear Power Plant Company (N.P.P.C.), one of four British groups set up to design and build complete nuclear stations. The other consortium members being Head Wrightson, Parsons, Reyrolle, McAlpine, Clark-Chapman, Alex Findlay and Strachan and Henshaw. Each member designed and tendered to N.P.P.C. for the components of the power station in which they had particular expertise.

Britain at that time had the largest nuclear electricity programme in the world and the Bradwell power station in Essex was the first major nuclear power station, for civil purposes, to be built anywhere.

The Central Electricity Generating Board (C.E.G.B.) awarded this "first" to N.P.P.C. and Whessoe became immediately involved in the research, development and design of the two reactor vessels (Whessoe's 9th and 10th), resulting in 66 ft. 9 in. diameter spheres in 3 in. and 4 in. thick steel plate. Again, because of the very high thermal and pressure stresses involved, a special steel was developed jointly by Whessoe and Consett Iron Co. This steel had modified ratios of carbon, manganese, silicon and aluminium to give improved strength, notch ductility and weldability essential for these high integrity vessels.

Incidentally the links between Consett Iron and Whessoe had been forged as far back as 1845 when orders were placed with Consett's precursors The Derwent Iron Co. for locomotive plates.

On the earlier reactor vessels, the thick plate had been pressed warm before erection and final welding on site, but with the new normalized plates hot pressing at normalizing temperature was essential.

When consideration was being given, therefore, to future projects under N.P.P.C. Whessoe decided to install its own hot press and invested some £750,000 in the Fielding 4,500 ton ram press, capable of hot pressing steel plates up to 12 inches thick. It was assumed that as more power was demanded nationally, designs would become more advanced, utilising even thicker plate.

The use of thicker plate also required the introduction of new welding techniques and 100 per cent radiographic and ultimately, ultrasonic examination of all weld seams and the ultrasonic examination of plate for laminations and cracking.

Work was started on Bradwell site in January 1957 and despite a slow down of activities for several months due to National financial restrictions the station was completed and commissioned in 1962.

In 1958 two additional important nuclear contracts were secured by Whessoe.

The N.P.P.C. consortium was awarded the contract for the first British export of a complete nuclear power station for Agip Nuclear at Latina, near Rome. Whessoe were to build the 67 ft. diameter spherical pressure vessel—the first such vessel to be built by any firm outside its own country.

The second contract was to build the pressure vessel for a new reactor of very advanced design at Windscale (now renamed Sellafield) near Calder Hall. This vessel was 21 ft. diameter with an overall height of 53 ft.

Both vessels were built in plate thicknesses up to $4\frac{3}{8}$ inches.

In addition to the pressure vessel Whessoe manufactured the thermal shield, the structure for supporting the core (Diagrid) and hot gas manifold (Hotbox).

The new Windscale reactor was the prototype for the new advanced Gas-cooled Reactors (A.G.R.s) and although of similar size to the Calder Hall reactors, had a capability of producing six times as much power. Differing little in general principle from the current power reactors except in its fuel elements, it was anticipated that this new type could be introduced fairly readily into the power programme and was regarded as the successor to the "Magnox" reactors for power stations going into operation in the 1960s.

I would not attempt to give a dissertation on the art and science of nuclear engineering. This can be found in many learned publications written by experienced nuclear engineers, but the following descriptions

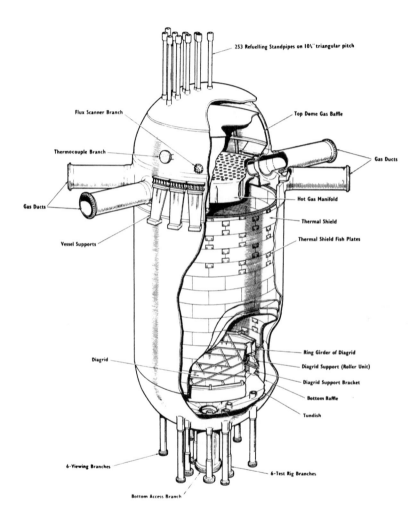

This diagramatic view of the Windscale Reactor gives an idea of the internal workings of the early nuclear pressure vessels designed and built by Whessoe.

of the operational principles of a thermal reactor may help the reader to understand better the design and fabrication problems met and overcome by Whessoe engineers.

A Nuclear Reactor is a way of generating heat to produce steam, to drive turbines, to generate electricity in much the same way as fossil fuelled power stations do.

The heat to generate steam comes from the fissile chain reactions, the temperature dependent upon the number of fissions taking place. Early Magnox reactors had their fuel in the form of a uranium bar about an inch in diameter, set in a "magnesium alloy" can—hence the name MAGNOX.

The fuel rods are located in a large graphite core and the fission generates heat which is absorbed by pressurised gas which then passes through boilers to heat water and generate wet steam at a temperature of around 300°C. to 400°C.

To become more efficient and to use the same type of turbines as fossil fired power stations, dry steam needed to be generated at temperatures around 600/650°C. This was not possible with magnesium alloy cans which tended to rupture at these higher temperatures. The new A.G.R. at Windscale used stainless steel cans containing uranium oxide pellets in place of metallic oxide fuel rods encased in magnox alloy, a complete change in the fuel elements, which was the principal new feature of A.G.R.s.

The Windscale reactor worked at three times the pressure of previous reactors and the diameter of the pressure vessel was restricted to 21 ft. diameter in order to keep steel plate thicknesses within the capability of the plate mills, which at that time was about 5 inches. Once again Conlo 1, the steel jointly developed by Whessoe and Consett Iron Co. was used. At the top end of the vessel 253 stand-pipes had to be fitted through the dome so that the fuel rods could be lifted in or out of the graphite core to control the nuclear fission. On the Bradwell reactor these stand-pipes were fitted within a 44 ft. diameter circle but on the Windscale reactor the same number had to go into a 15 ft. circle.

The boring of so many holes and subsequent welding on of the stand-pipes posed tremendous problems in distortion and sinkage of the dome. So eventually the dome plates were completely welded together, X-rayed and stress relieved as a unit on site to relax heavy butt welded stresses.

The steel plate around the stand-pipe area was thickened up to avoid building up the reinforcement thickness of the stand-pipe stub ends and thus the attachment weld sizes were reduced.

The 253 stand-pipe holes were marked out on a $10\frac{1}{4}$ in. triangular pitch with a positional accuracy of 0.024 inch. The vertical axis of each hole through the bottom of the 60 ft. high vessel had to be maintained to within $\frac{1}{8}$ in. which demanded great skills in plating, welding and dimensional surveying.

In operation the outlet gases from the core were too hot to be allowed to impinge on the pressure vessel shell, so a collection box was put above the graphite core (the hot gas manifold, or Hotbox). This was virtually another pressure vessel with a differential pressure of 30 p.s.i.g. and exposed to temperatures of 650°C.

So that it would operate at the same temperature as the top dome the box was insulated with stainless steel, a major and tricky operation since it had to be done under rigorous conditions of cleanliness. This work was done in the Darlington Works within a vacuum controlled purpose built building.

In addition to these problems a thermal shield had to be fitted inside the reactor to minimise neutron leakage from the core and avoid direct leakage paths. This shield was made from three layers of overlapping 2 in. thick mild steel plate, rolled and welded into cylinders of approximately 20 ft. diameter.

At the bottom of the vessel a support structure was installed to support the weight of the heavy graphite core, which could weigh up to 4,000 tons. This structure known as the Diagrid was fabricated from heavy sections of steel plate, criss-crossed for strength but demanding a high concentration of heavy full penetration welds with all their inherent problems of distortion and cracking.

All of the techniques for the fabrication of these new complicated reactors were developed within Whessoe and the Company was seen to be the leading manufacturer of this equipment in the world at that time.

The principles of all future nuclear reactors remained the same but the designs and fabrication became more onerous as output requirements and safety standards increased in leaps and bounds.

Whessoe continued to build nuclear reactor vessels, through the association with T.N.P.G. (The Nuclear Power Group), formed in 1959 through a merger of N.P.P.C. and the A.E.I./John Thompson Group, which at the time were the two strongest nuclear power construction groups.

The first T.N.P.G. tender was for the new Dungeness "A" power station in Essex which had two reactors, giving an increased capacity of 550 MW. The order from C.E.G.B. was received in the summer of 1960 and were Whessoe's 13th and 14th reactor vessels—the last of the thick wall vessels to be built by Whessoe.

Next followed an order for the cylindrical containment vessel for the Dragon reactor at Winfrith.

In 1962 T.N.P.G received the order for Oldbury power station which incorporated a complete redesign of the pressure containment vessel based on a pre-stressed concrete pressure shell with the inside surfaces protected by a relatively thin steel containment liner ($\frac{1}{2}$ in.), insulated and cooled to protect the concrete.

This new design made less use of our 4,500 ton ram press as it was only required for the thicker steel domes and it was never subsequently used to its full pressing capacity. Still, we had to move with the times and Whessoe concentrated on developing new design principles and manufacturing techniques for this liner, since the steel was operating in its compressive yield range, an entirely novel situation.

Special jigs and welding sequences were developed for the controlled welding of miles of cooling water pipes. These had to be welded to the outside surfaces of the mild steel liner plates prior to their erection and welding into the cylindrical containment vessel. Eventually they were to be surrounded by several metres of pre-stressed concrete.

After Oldbury came an order for two 96ft. diameter spherical steel liners for the pre-stressed concrete reactor vessels for the Wylfa "A" Power station in Wales. This power station order (which was then the world's most powerful with a design capacity of 1,180 MW.) was won

Moving into position the Whessoe-built steel liner of the pre-stressed concrete pressure vessel at Oldbury Nuclear Power Station.

from C.E.G.B. by N.D.C. a rival consortium, but they placed the liners with Whessoe because of their undoubted expertise in this area.

Orders for further power stations were won through the 1960s, for Hinkley "B", Hunterston "B", Dungeness"B" and Heysham "A", making a total of 26 reactor vessels completed by Whessoe out of a national total at that time of 36, again a very impressive record.

Incidentally, the Dungeness "B" reactors were actually placed with one of the other consortia who ran into serious fabrication problems during the build of the liners.

Whessoe were asked for advice on a rectification procedure and eventually took in hand the repair work which entailed scrapping the complete liner except for the floor and first wall section. This brought Whessoe world-wide publicity within the nuclear industry and resulted in licence agreements with Kawasaki (Japan). Steinmuller (Germany) and Foster Wheeler (U.S.A.).

There were no further orders placed for nuclear power stations in the U.K. during the 1970s whilst the Government re-thought the future of the Nuclear Programme.

Original thoughts were, that following the assumed successful outcome of the A.G.R. programme, in terms of power output, a new design of H.T.R. (High Temperature Reactor) would follow. This was dropped,

The 96 ft. diameter bottom hemisphere of the nuclear reactor containment vessel being lowered into position at the 1180 Mw nuclear power station at Wylfa, Anglesy, Wales.

however, in favour of the S.G.H.W.R. (Steam Generating Heavy Water Reactor) and Whessoe received a development contract to determine fabrication procedures for the new containment liners which were to be made of a special stainless steel material. Experimental heavy water reactors had been built in the early 1950s at the Atomic Energy Research Establishment at Harwell and Whessoe had provided a detailed design study for a Sealed Building to enclose the Nuclear Pile. The Ministry of Works eventually placed orders direct with Whessoe for a special steel-domed Sealed Building 67 ft. diameter × 70 ft. high for each of their DIDO and PLUTO reactors.

The S.G.H.W.R. programme, however, was also eventually revoked in 1976 and to prevent the total collapse of the nuclear programme and the loss of the expensively gained expertise two more A.G.R. type power stations were ordered in 1979.

These were for Heysham "B" in Lancashire and Torness in Southern Scotland and both were placed with T.N.P.G and Whessoe. At the same time the door was opened for the possibility of using the American P.W.R. (Pressurised Water Reactor).

The manufacturing procedures for these last four A.G.R. reactors will be dealt with later in the book but when completed they brought Whessoe's total up to thirty-four out of the final overall U.K. total of forty-two separate reactors.

They saw, however, the end of Whessoe's nuclear involvement, as the only other nuclear power station to be commissioned will be the P.W.R. at Sizewell "B" currently in hand, with most of the pressure components being placed elsewhere in Europe. Only the high pressure pipework was made available to the Whessoe Group through their subsidiary Aiton of Derby. The advent of the gas fired power stations may well see the end of commercial nuclear power production activities in Britain, but that remains to be seen. The fifties decade saw a tremendous leap forward by Whessoe in terms of order achievement and productivity in the bread and butter items of tanks, pressure vessels and heat exchangers, in addition to the new major products outlined in this section, wind tunnels and nuclear power.

The publicity surrounding the nuclear vessels tended to overshadow other products but they must not be ignored in chronicling Whessoe's history. Nor must certain events that to a large extent changed the course of the history and the structure of the Company.

A contract of significant importance that tended to be overlooked was the design, fabrication, erection and testing of a jet engine testing facility at Pyestock near Farnborough, the site of the National Gas Turbine Establishment, where a great deal of the early development work of gas-turbines for jet propulsion had been done by Sir Frank Whittle and his team of engineers. This new facility was designed to test all types of gas-turbines, jet engines and ram jet engines.

Whessoe was responsible for the design and manufacture of nearly all the pressure steelwork, involving over 2,000 tons of fabricated steel cylinders with diameters varying from 7 feet to 30 feet and a total length of several hundred feet.

The operating conditions covered a temperature range of minus 70°C to plus 1,750°C, pressures from 162 p.s.i.g. to full vacuum and simulated air speeds up to 2,000 m.p.h. demanding the resolution of many complicated design problems in order to cope with the resultant thermal and pressure stresses.

Over the years Whessoe has provided storage facilities for most things from petrol/oil to gas and even soap. One of the most unusual tasks was convincing McDougalls the flour people to change from concrete silos for the storage of wheat and flour to fabricated steel silos which we were convinced would be more economical in terms of capital outlay, particularly with the savings on huge foundations required for concrete silos.

The major objection to steel was its tendency to sweat with temperature changes. Moisture would cause dry wheat to ferment and the resultant heat and pressure set up would have been tremendous. Whessoe solved this problem by the application of a special painted coating to the internal surfaces and McDougalls eventually awarded a contract to Whessoe for two large steel silos 55 ft. diameter by 70 ft. high each holding 3,250 tons of dry wheat.

In 1956 a piece of land on the river Tees at Middlesborough was leased to allow for the assembly of large fabrications prior to shipment overseas. This site called the Cleveland site, was later to be extended and known as Dock Point, a major facility for Whessoe's future Offshore activities.

Gas-plant production flourished maintaining Whessoe's reputation in that field with 375 plants being completed since the 1930s and supplied to some nineteen countries.

The year 1957 brought a record output of site built spheres and heat exchanger production was at full capacity. The Shand & Jurs business continued to expand and plans were being developed for the building of a factory in France and the setting up of Whessoe S.A.-Calais, a wholly owned subsidiary of Whessoe Limited, Darlington.

Despite this flurry of activity, however, by the end of 1957 there were signs appearing of a recession in the engineering industry. Whessoe and the nation were very much at the crossroads. It became clear that since the end of the war Britain and most other countries had been trying to do too much too quickly.

During the past ten years Whessoe had expanded along with many of their competitors and other countries had started doing their own engineering. As a result, with falling demands, there were more suppliers and never since the war had there been such fierce competition.

For the first time in twenty years Whessoe had few orders. Rumours of redundancy were rife, although unfounded. As a result tension developed, particularly on sites. Counter-productive strikes and slow downs started to develop with the loss of thousands of man-hours at a time when the maintenance of completion dates was vital to retain the Company's good name.

Many hours of negotiation took place between management and unions. By careful planning and cuts in overtime working Whessoe managed to retain all its labour force, working 44 hours a week without any redundancies or lay-offs. Despite this concern about deteriorating work loads throughout the Company and indeed nationally, Whessoe management took an optimistic view and continued with investment in new buildings and equipment.

In 1958 the front aspect of the Darlington Works was re-organized including the newly acquired land purchased from British Railways.

Before this area could be cleared a new canteen had to be built to replace the one used by the Railway staff and a medical centre was built at the same time.

On the cleared land an erection area was established, to be known as the Low Field. The new three storey Shand & Jurs building was erected, incorporating offices and workshops for the rapidly expanding business.

The new No.2 Welding Shop was completed at the north end of the site and new machine tools including lathes and milling machines were purchased. The first electronic calculating and punch card machines (the fore runners of the computer) were installed in the Accounts department.

Around this time there were other influences which had an affect upon management strategy.

In 1920 the private Whessoe Company had gone public and Shell bought 51 per cent of the Ordinary shares, giving them a controlling financial interest. At the time this was of considerable benefit to Whessoe as it opened up the route for orders from the petroleum industry.

In 1957, when most of the current refinery development and expansions had been completed, Shell relinquished their majority holding. The shares were bought up in smaller packages, mostly by insurance companies, leaving Whessoe free to develop and manage their own business.

Coincidentally, 1957 was the diamond jubilee of both Shells' Foundation in April 1897 and the diamond jubilee of Whessoe's first order for two railway turn-tables, from Marcus Samuel the founder of Shell.

Interestingly, Whessoe's very first order connected with the petroleum industry was in 1891 for "48—Loose box mangers" from the Anglo—American Oil Co. who used horse drawn drays to transport paraffin oil throughout the U.K.

It was for Anglo-American that Whessoe evolved the 9 ft. × 30 ft. shop built tanks and continued to supply them to Anglo-American under their new name of ESSO.

ESSO opened a new refinery at Fawley on Southampton Water in
1957 alongside 1,000 acres of existing petroleum plant, much of which
had been supplied by Whessoe.

In the first five years of this new refinery development, Whessoe
built forty storage tanks and seven spheres and continued with similar
work when ESSO opened another new refinery at Milford Haven on
the Pembrokeshire coast.

By this time H.G.Judd who had been the Whessoe Chairman for
thirty-five years since 1920 retired and his place was taken by Claude
Spielman. A new face appeared on the Main Board, that of Michael
Noone, who had started with Whessoe in 1934 as a plant engineer,
later becoming welding engineer, chief draughtsman, chief engineer
and then Manager of Operations.

M.N. as he was known was responsible for much of the engineering
advances made by Whessoe and led the Company's entry into the design
and building of large site built pressure vessels, refinery plant, nuclear
reactors and wind tunnels.

To combat the current problems of the highly competitive market
the Managing Director, A.G. Grant, assisted by M.N. and other senior
managers, evolved a major re-organization of Whessoe by moving away
from the traditional horizontal management structure to Vertical
Grouping with three Divisions.

The Works Division and the Construction Division were placed
under the management of Mr. Reg. Slater and Mr. Arthur Nelson
respectively and a new Engineering Division was formed under Mr.
Ron Bishop.

The Engineering Division had three Groups, one under Donald
Hudspeth dealt with tanks and storage, another under Ron Horseman
dealt with pressure vessels, large and small. The third Group dealt with
chemical engineering and was headed by Mr. Jack Thompson a new
recruit to the Company.

Each Group was self contained with estimators, designers, draughtsmen, engineers of various skills, clerks and typists. In this way it was
hoped to concentrate the efforts on particular products, make tendering
more efficient and build up the order books again.

Although this new organization took some time to develop and settle down, it appeared to do the trick. The success ratio between tenders and orders improved, with the order book advancing from a forward work load of only five months to one of twelve months.

The nuclear orders in the late fifties, and a new round of refinery expansion work, meant that by the end of the decade the recession seemed to have been reversed and Whessoe's capacity was fully taken up in both Works and on the Sites. Tankage took up 60 per cent, pressure vessels, reactors and wind tunnels 20 per cent, and heat exchangers, gas plant and S. & J. fittings the other 20 per cent.

Things looked good for the immediate future.

There was one other significant factor that was going to influence Whessoe's future—after three years of study I had passed my Ordinary National Certificate in both Production and Mechanical Engineering and was ready to offer my indispensable services to the Whessoe management!!!

9

The Nineteen Sixties

The year 1960 was going to see a major step forward in my life and career, or so I believed. Having made the effort and achieved the first stage in my technical education I then had to decide how I was going to make best use of it. What could I do or, more important, what had I to offer?

I was a mature person (aged 30) had a good practical experience of many Whessoe products, had a minor engineering qualification, still being developed, and had the will and desire to learn.

The estimating department seemed to be the opportunity and I made a direct approach to the Chief Estimator asking for the opportunity to train as an estimator. He appeared to be impressed with my attitude and said he would consider and let me know in due course whether there were any vacancies.

After several weeks without a response I again approached him but was advised that, although there was a vacancy and I appeared to be suitable, my movement from the Works had been blocked by the Works Manager on the basis that I was more useful where I was.

Not to be out done I then cast around for an opportunity outside the Whessoe environment and obtained an interview with a local company making mining equipment and was offered a position as an estimator with an immediate start. Having satisfied myself that I was employable I still had that unaccountable desire to stay with Whessoe and made one last approach on the basis that I was going to leave the Works in any case so why not make use of me somewhere else.

I was asked to go over my educational history again and this time mentioned the nine months I had spent at the Grammar School in Hull which brought about an almost magical change of attitude—"why hadn't I mentioned before that I was a Grammar School boy?"

This could be the key to my staff employment.

One week later I was summoned to an interview in front of four senior managers and the personnel officer (a bit over the top I thought) and was finally offered a job as a trainee estimator on six months probation at the salary of £760 per year.

I had to think about this seriously as my current earnings with some overtime on the shop floor were about £1,000. Acceptance meant a 25 per cent cut in salary, but what the hell, I couldn't give up now so I accepted and made that Quantum Leap from Works to Staff.

Four weeks later I left the shop floor for good and started as an estimator on the Heat Exchanger section led by a dominant character, Harry Bundy. Incidentally, one of the senior estimators on the section was my old pal Ray Rocket of Bomb Room fame.

Although I was now where I wanted to be and had worked for, the first few months were a difficult period. It was a totally different working environment from the Works and it took some time to settle in, my office boy period being long forgotten.

Fortunately, as I mentioned earlier, relationships between Works and staff had improved over the recent years, as indeed had my own attitude and understanding and the fact that the majority of estimators in our section had been time served craftsmen helped to smooth the transition for me. Everyone, without exception, was very helpful and made every effort to teach me the new trade. There is no doubt that the last three years of technical education had opened my mind, allowing it to absorb a lot of new information in a relatively short time.

Heat exchangers were very complex pieces of equipment with a multiplicity of design requirements necessary to cope with temperature, pressure and corrosion environments. The range of materials used in their manufacture was almost endless. Their compositions were controlled by detailed specifications, mainly of American origin and published in annually up-dated volumes of A.S.T.M. (American Society for Testing of Materials) manuals.

I started my training by checking other estimates so that I got used to the procedure and eventually was able to put together my own tenders, but I made it my business to learn everything I could about materials and manufacturing techniques. Reading had always been a passion of mine and swotting up on the A.S.T.M. and A.S.M.E. design codes was not really a problem, and I had a lot of years to make up.

My own experiences on the shop floor with heat exchangers obviously was a tremendous help in reading and understanding the drawings and designs, although designs had progressed tremendously since those earlier years in the 1950s. In the intervening ten years the heat exchanger market had developed. Whereas Whessoe had been looking at orders for one or two exchangers at a time, based on other peoples designs, we were now dealing with quite substantial numbers from any one customer, as refinery and chemical plants were installed or extended and in many cases using our own thermal and mechanical designs.

As the Company extended its market areas and tendering activities, the one department that was always busy was Estimating.

Enquiries were flooding in as Whessoe's reputation for quality and performance became internationally known. With a highly competitive market the success ratio of tenders to orders was 14:1 which meant an awful lot of tenders had to be produced. Most estimators at that time worked a regular two nights a week overtime and sometimes week-ends when urgent tenders were due.

The extra money of course was very useful to me in view of my reduced income. But, once again, three nights a week at night school, which I needed to continue for a further two years to get my Higher National Certificate, prevented me from taking advantage of the overtime opportunity. Because of my particular circumstances, Harry Bundy arranged for me to do my overtime stint by starting each day at 7.30 a.m. for which I was very grateful.

Harry Bundy was a hard taskmaster but a very helpful one. As soon as he accepted that I was intent on learning the business and progressing myself he set about knocking off all my rough edges, pushing more work on me and criticizing everything I did. No letter I wrote or tender I prepared was ever right. Regularly, he would ask how many jobs I had on and if in desperation I said "seven" he would reply with "well here is the eighth". All the time he was pushing more and more information into me, ensuring that I got through my six month probation period.

I think Harry Bundy, more than anyone, was responsible for directing my future career and giving me the necessary confidence in myself and a good grasp of the commercial and business world.

I stayed with heat exchanger estimating for just over three years. Having had my salary increased to a reasonable level and having obtained my Higher National I started to look for further advancement.

During this three year period, however, life had not been standing still in other areas of Whessoe. Despite the increase in heat exchanger, nuclear reactor and Shand and Jurs activities, other product lines were having problems with reduced demands—particularly tankage and thus site construction activity.

The Management had been exploring several avenues in an effort to develop new products or to expand existing ones to cover larger market areas. But before making any drastic changes they engaged McKinsey & Co., a firm of international business consultants to review the Company's business and market prospects. Their thoughts were pretty similar to those of the Management but entailed major structural changes that would take some time to put in place.

Basically, it was considered the right time to diversify lines of activity so that all the eggs were not in one basket. When one product was up, another might be down but hopefully not all down together. A pretty basic strategy, it would now appear, but one that was taken up.

Another important suggestion was to concentrate on some products with a bigger element of know-how which should reduce competition.

During the next twelve months Whessoe negotiated a licence to manufacture Air-Blown heat exchangers from G.E.A. of Germany. G.E.A. later withdrew and the decision was taken to go it alone. It was seen as a good opportunity to expand and develop the heat exchanger market into areas and countries that did not have the water supplies necessary for some conventional exchangers.

One of over 1,300 Butane Storage Spheres nicknamed 'Sputniks', ready for despatch.

An agreement was also reached with the Selas Co. of America to allow Whessoe to design, manufacture and install Gradation Furnaces. These furnaces were used in refineries for heating petroleum oils at the inlet to distillation columns, cat crackers and various reforming processes.

In the Works at Darlington contracts were being won for Whessoe designed butane storage spheres aptly named at that time "Sputniks" due to their similarity to the Russian space craft currently in orbit. The Sputniks were steel segmented spheres 4 ft. 9 in. diameter on a tubular stand, designed to hold 1,500 lbs. of propane or butane gas at 225 p.s.i.g. They were jig built and welded on special manipulators with all seams being radiographed using an Iridium 192 Isotope probe.

Several hundreds of these were made and proved to be quite a lucrative production line item. They were used to heat poultry houses, canteen kitchens and for supplying welders with gas for pre-heating as well as providing the fuel for small furnaces. With their small size and weight (0.6 tons) they were easily transportable and could be filled from road tankers.

They were probably the nearest Whessoe got to manufacturing for the consumer market, which meant that appearance was everything so they were shot blasted, zinc sprayed and given a final finishing coat of special paint with identity marks and logos.

At this same time, despite the shortage of large vessel orders but in order to secure the production output for the next decade, the decision to go ahead with the building of a new large welding shop was ratified. The shop was to be the largest in the Company being 555 ft. long, by 86 ft. wide, by 54 ft. high to the roof and was to cost £500,000. It was served by two 50 ton overhead cranes which, when used together, had a maximum lift of 125 tons.

An extension to the main shop included for the largest stress relieving furnace in Europe being 80 ft. long, by 18 ft. square with a load capacity of 200 tons. It had a controlled temperature range from 400°C to 1150°C and was heated by town gas.

Adjoining the furnace building was a concrete X-ray compound designed to give full radiation protection for a million volt X-ray source.

The shop went into production in September 1961 with a contract for the largest heat exchangers yet built being 9 ft. diameter, by 36 ft. long for an export contract to Assam in India. The official opening was conducted in November 1961 by the Rt. Hon. Frederick Erroll

Whessoe's new welding shop, incorporating Europe's largest stress relieving furnace and x-ray compound. At 555 ft. by 86 ft. wide the shop has become a major landmark in the locality.

M.P. the then Minister for the Board of Trade, subsequently, as Lord
Errol of Hale, to become Whessoe's Chairman, succeeding J.H. Lord.

In the month following the opening of the new shop there was a
major change in the executive management with the early retirement
of A. G. Grant at the age of 58 following an extended period of ill
health. He came to Whessoe in the 1930s as Technical Assistant to the
then Managing Direction R.B. Hodgson, was appointed General Manager in 1942 and M.D. in 1954.

His place was taken by a dual appointment of M. Noone and S.R.
Chetwynd Archer as Joint General Managers.

New product lines were still being considered. The Research & Development department, headed by R.F. Bishop, was examining products
involving some diversification from the conventional steel fabrications
and in 1960 a separate department was established within the Darlington

*Two 13 ft. diameter by 20 ft. high glass fibre wine storage tanks
designed and manufactured by Whessoe plastics.*

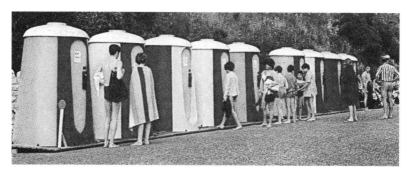

Reinforced plastic beach huts designed and built by Whessoe plastics for South Coast resorts.

Works to investigate the manufacture of storage tanks using plastic materials, particularly those involving glass-fibre-reinforced resins.

Considerable effort was devoted to the physical and chemical testing of materials, the building up of design information and the development of production techniques. Following the manufacture of prototype vessels, customer enquiries were sought and orders obtained for initially, conventional cylindrical tanks with dished ends.

The department extended its range of products to cover such items as hoppers, scrubbing towers, chimneys, cyclones, and ducts and pipework until eventually the existing production officialities became inadequate. In late 1962 production commenced in the Plastics Factory at Crook, County Durham. Almost immediately these premises were extended and in 1963 The Plastics Division was created with both its Works and Offices at Crook.

The range of products became considerably wider than had been originally envisaged and a proportion of the production was devoted to less technical products such as beach huts, chalets and boats. Some of the beach huts are still in use at South Coast resorts.

In 1964 an order was received from Thornycroft Island Cruisers Ltd. for the manufacture and assembly of 1,000 glass-fibre "Tomkat" Catamarans. The twin pontoons were made from war surplus torpedo-shaped aircraft jettison tanks coated with plastic and were fitted with sails or power units. Under trials the prototype craft achieved certified speeds of 42 k.p.h. when fitted with a 40 h.p. outboard motor.

*Whessoe Plastics manufactured 1,000 glass fibre catamarans for
Thornycroft Island Cruisers, Ltd. They were fitted with sails or 40 h.p.
outboard motors.*

With established cylindrical pressure vessel designs for static requirements, it was not long before transportable tanks were seen as a
viable proposition. Over the next few years Whessoe designed and built
reinforced plastic road tankers for the transport of beer, edible oils,
tallow, fuel oils, quenching oils, transformer oils, cement additives,
acids, resins and water. The range covered rigid, semi-trailer and ar-
ticulated units of circular, elliptical and box-section shapes.

These vessels had capacities up to 5,000 gallons, operating at pressure
of 30 p.s.i.g. and some of the static tanks were 30 ft. long and 14 ft.
diameter with capacities of 29,000 gallons.

The Plastics Division remained a progressive unit until a change of
Managing Director brought about policy changes and the Crook factory
was finally closed and sold off in 1968 having introduced many inno-
vative designs and procedures into the plastic industry.

In 1956 Whessoe purchased the three acres of land they had leased
from Middlesbrough Estates a year earlier. An order had been won for
several large vessels and circular sections for Polaris Submarine hulls

which were outside the Darlington capacity. The Cleveland site seemed an ideal acquisition for this type of work.

The site was actually a triangular strip of land adjacent to the Middlesbrough Docks and known locally as Dock Point. The land was levelled, hard core laid, and a 220 ft. × 40 ft. wide sliding shop was transferred from the Bradwell site and erected beneath the 40 ton Goliath travelling crane also transferred from Bradwell. A total of thirty-eight large vessels kept the site going into mid 1961 and over the ensuing years more land was purchased or leased, extending it to a 31 acre site operated by the Erection Department. This eventually led to the formation of Whessoe's Offshore activities.

Another acquisition opportunity arose in 1962 with the purchase of Express Tools Ltd. of Chessington, Surrey. This Company was owned by Mettoy Ltd. the toy maker and were makers of precision jigs and tools. Only 10 per cent of its work was for the toy industry at the time of the take-over. Most of its work was contract work making jigs and tools for customers like Rolls-Royce, Bristol Siddely Engines, Plessey and Singer etc.

It was seen as a welcome addition to the Light Engineering aspects of Whessoe, allied to the Shand & Jurs facility.

During 1962 work picked up to a large extent, particularly in the heat exchanger field with over 180 exchangers and tube bundles being built in the year, an average of 3.5 exchangers per week, many of them in difficult chrome alloy materials. To cope with this upsurge in business Whessoe purchased the Stooperdale railway works adjacent to the west boundary fence bringing another eight shops into use.

The tank fitting business was also proving to be a very profitable concern and the newly opened Calais Works was drawing in much work from the Continent or the Common Market as it was then becoming known.

Although Whessoe had developed many methods of storing liquids, solids and gases, one of the most problematic storage requirements had been the containment of certain gases.

Ammonia, butane, chlorine, ethane, hydrogen, methane, nitrogen, oxygen and propane are all normally gaseous under atmospheric conditions but at sub-normal or extremely low temperatures are in liquid phase. Refrigerated storage was seen as a sensible and practical way of storing such gases. Whessoe carried out essential development and experimental work in the Research and Development Division at Darlington where new fabrication and construction techniques were developed and complex but economic refrigeration designs conceived and tested.

The very first contract for refrigerated storage was placed in 1959 by the North Thames Gas Board for an experimental scheme at Canvey Island. Whessoe were responsible for the complete design, fabrication and construction of a 1,000 ton capacity liquid methane storage tank.

The tank consisted of a 100 ft. diameter mild steel outer shell within which was a 95 ft. diameter ring stiffened, aluminium liquid container. The base of this was mounted on foam-glass insulation, the outer wall clad with a fibre-glass mattress and the interspace filled with Perlite.

The gas inlet and outlet connections were kept at the top of the vessel and the liquid outlet connection at the base. This particular tank was to be filled from deep sea L.N.G. tankers and was used as the bulk storage for feeding an adjacent liquid methane evaporation plant again designed and built by Whessoe.

This storage tank although experimental operated very efficiently and in 1961 a further five tanks each 4,000 ton capacity were placed with Whessoe for the same site.

Over the next ten years Whessoe designed and built around sixty refrigerated storage tanks and several spheres, eleven of these being Turnkey Projects including the associated refrigeration plants and transfer equipment. They covered the storage of ammonia through to oxygen and nitrogen at refrigerated temperatures of minus 33°C to minus 183°C. They were supplied not only within the U.K. but also to Argentina, Australia, Holland, Mexico, Singapore and South Africa.

As experience was gained over the ensuing years the tanks, especially those used for the storage of ethylene, became larger and more complex with suspended insulated roofs. Those used for oxygen and nitrogen in particular, involved more exotic materials for the inner tanks such as 9 per cent nickel and 18/8 stainless steels as well as aluminium.

Low temperature storage in spheres was covered by again using double shells. One of the largest being an ethylene storage sphere built by Whessoe at Esso Fawley refinery. The 62 feet. diameter mild steel outer sphere contained an aluminium inner shell which gave a storage capacity of 1,700 tons of ethylene at a working temperature of minus 104°C.

Although other fabricators were becoming more involved in cryogenic storage there was no doubt that Whessoe were the leaders in the field. They were called upon for consultancy work with the main Gas Boards, for their natural gas development, and by I.C.I. and oil companies. Licence agreements were also negotiated with Japanese and German organisations who were well behind in the cryogenic field.

About this time, with the expansion of the Whessoe Group in mind and following the full appraisal of the McKinsey report, a further restructuring programme was put in hand and Whessoe was divided into five separate Divisions, three Operating divisions and two Service divisions.

The main area covering the core business was called the Heavy Equipment Division under Michael Noone as Direction and General Manager. Then came the Engineering Services Division and the Light Products Division. The Service divisions were Research & Development and Finance & Administration.

Following the implementation of these structural changes Mr. Chetwynd Archer resigned and Michael Noone was appointed Group Managing Director.

The Board was still looking at ways of extending existing product lines and tankage was always particularly subject to peaks and troughs due to market fluctuations. An opportunity to get into the smaller tankage market presented itself with the purchase of a small fabrication company in Southern Ireland.

Universal Fabricators Ltd. was situated at Finglas north of Dublin and concentrated on the manufacture of rainwater goods, small gauge tanks of the order of 300 gallon capacity and some low pressure vessels up to 12,000 gallon capacity.

On certain aspects of their work particular items such as roof trusses and pressurised tanks required specialized designs and Whessoe had been approached on several occasions for assistance and guidance in design and fabrication procedures by the then owner, an Englishman by the name of Reynolds, who was basically a scrap dealer and Chairman of Leeds United football team in that order.

It was obvious that an injection of cash was badly needed and Whessoe Board negotiated the purchase and took overall control of the Company in 1964.

It was an opportunity to extend the Whessoe tankage business into the more competitive lighter and smaller end of the market without the penalty of the much higher Darlington overheads.

At the time of purchase the Company, which was large by Irish standards, employed 200 people in the Works and Outside Erection department. There was a permanent core of about twenty staff with additional labour being recruited as the work load demanded.

Existing equipment was minimal and this was quickly supplemented by the installation of a set of heavy plate rolls, a vertical press complete with its own furnace for the pressing of dished ends, a stress relieving furnace and pickling baths for tank plates.

The office area was enlarged to extend the design and engineering capabilities and the facility was quickly capable of manufacturing Class 1 pressure vessels and tank sizes increased from the previous maximum of 48 ft. diameter using $5/16$ in. thick plate to 180 ft. diameter with $1/2$ in. and $5/8$ in. plate.

The first order for such tanks was from the Dublin Electricity Supply Board and was the largest order ever placed by the Board. The tanks had a total capacity of 115,000 gallons and used 3,000 tons of steel. The thick plates were edge-prepped on a large automated burning machine installed for the purpose.

Prior to the Whessoe take-over, erection work had only been done in Southern Ireland but this was expanded into Northern Ireland, having first overcome the reluctance of the local labour to work in that area in view of the troubles.

Work was exported overseas and eventually complete vessels and tanks were shipped to mainland England securing work in a market hitherto unobtainable.

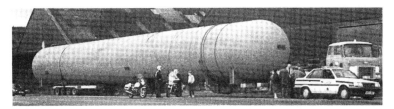

Ireland's largest pressure vessel, 130 ft. long and 12 ft. diameter en-route to Belfast.

Whessoe (I) Ltd. continued for over thirty years as a valued part of the Whessoe Group until finally being purchased as a management buy-out by the incumbent Managing Director Martin McEvoy in 1992.

The design and engineering sections at Darlington were seen as support groups for the Works business but for many years Whessoe had built complete plants for the Process industry and had also carried out "engineering only" contracts for this type of project. The Process department, part of the Chemical Division, under the leadership of Jack Thompson and augmented by the engineering and other resources of the Company carried out complete engineering and project management of such contracts.

The Gas Boards were looking seriously at conversion from town's gas to natural gas which required new process and reforming plants and Whessoe undertook the process design based on its own know-how and experience or arising from licence agreements.

Business developed rapidly and a new subsidiary company, Whessoe Projects and Engineering Limited (W.P.E.L.) was formed recruiting its own engineers and administrative staff, taking on multimillion pound Turnkey contracts.

The processes offered included gas drying, CO_2 and H_2S removal, desulphurization of hydrocarbons, sulphur recovery and the manufacture of substitute natural gas. The latter being the basis for a major contract with the Southern Gas Board at Bicester and Portsmouth.

In ten years to the mid 1970s, when North Sea gas eliminated the need for modifications to town's gas plants, W.P.E.L. completed over fifteen major Turnkey projects valued at over £25. million pounds, a valuable asset.

In 1967 Whessoe purchased the Teesside Works of Ashmore Benson and Pease. The complex covered a 64 acre site near Stockton, midway between Darlington and Middlesbrough, with easy access to the A19 trunk road and Middlesbrough Docks.

It had 245,000 sq.ft. of covered fabrication shops with bays, 520 ft. long × 65 ft. wide. The whole area being served by twenty-two overhead cranes with lifting capacities from 15 tons to 100 tons.

There were heavy and light machine shops with a total floor area of 150,000 sq. ft. again served by 100 ton overhead cranes.

The heavy face lathes were capable of handling 100 ton pieces and large vertical boring machines had maximum swings of 30 feet and could take loads up to 60 tons. It was a tremendous addition to the Whessoe Group allowing them to cope with machined fabrications outside the Darlington Works capacity.

The Iron and Steel industry provided the core of activity in the early years but major contracts were being carried out for all types of heavy industrial plant and machinery for the chemical, gas, and petroleum industries to all the major National and International Codes.

The machining of many components for the nuclear industry, previously sublet to other outside contractors, was transferred to the Stockton Works and several new products were introduced, not the least being M & J Valves, which were licensed from America. These were heavy fabricated gate valves up to 42 inches diameter used in high pressure gas and oil lines. They were operated by bevel gears and electric valve actuators and demanded a high degree of accuracy in assembly and machining.

I think one of the major and most significant acquisitions was that of Aiton & Co. Ltd. of Derby with its Canadian and Australian subsidiaries. It arose from the determination of one John Marshal Aiton, whose father had founded the company in January 1900, to safeguard his company, upon his demise, against falling into the hands of people he would not like controlling the family business and a possible forced sale due to crippling Estate Duty liabilities. In order to preserve, so

Trial assembly at the Whessoe Stockton works of one of the largest ball grinding mills to be made in the UK. The mill weighed 250 tons and was designed to grind 230 tons of copper ore per hour.

far as possible, the independent and self governing status of the Company a merger was agreed and they became a member of the Whessoe Group, retaining the Company name of Aiton.

Aiton's core business has always been the design and manufacture of piping systems concerned with the transmission of steam and water at the highest pressures and temperatures. It started with pipework used at sea in marine propulsion, progressing into heating pipework for department stores, hotels and hospitals, the first such job being for Harrods of London.

They then evolved, through increases in temperature, pressure and output requirements, to a major base load of pipework for fossil fired power stations and, latterly, nuclear power station systems, an area of particular interest to Whessoe in view of their considerable involvement in the nuclear scene.

Aiton very wisely had also developed other products to supplement the peaks and troughs of pipework contracts and moved into water distillation evaporator plants, mainly for the marine industry. In the 1950s and 60s they did an enormous amount of business providing evaporators to the newly nationalized power utilities in the U.K. Most of the stations were on the riverside and the evaporators were used to convert river water into chemically pure water for make-up to the closed feed systems.

Chemical treatment processes and the fall off in the number of conventional power stations being built made evaporators less relevant and Aiton moved into the manufacture of desalination plants. In the oil boom years of the 1970s the arid Middle East was a prime target. Aiton became one of only two U.K. companies supported by the British Government for desalination development.

Both the evaporator and desalination unit designs had close links with the heat transfer work being done by Whessoe's own heat exchanger department and both companies liaised and learned a lot from each other in these areas.

The heat transfer knowledge was used for other bespoke plants, from sewage sludge concentration to crystallizers and steam transformers and later developed complete drain and condensate systems, culminating in a successful contract for the decay systems used in nuclear power stations at Heysham and Torness.

The involvement in process plant brought Aiton into the agitator (mixer) manufacturing field and they became the licensee of Chemineer Inc. of Dayton Ohio (this was disposed of in 1973 when the Company was rationalizing the overall business).

Many of the new attempts at diversification were risky. Although many were successful there was no continuity of work and there was a tendency, therefore, to revert back to the core business of pipework manufacture which had progressed dramatically in the latter years with sophisticated computer design techniques.

The decision of the British Government to abandon A.G.R. reactors and build an American P.W.R. created an opportunity subsequently to prove to be of immense value to Aiton in particular and the Whessoe Group as a whole, despite the loss of the vessel fabrication and construction work.

C.E.G.B.'s desire to transfer P.W.R. expertise and technology to the U.K. caused them to seek design assistance from piping contractors. Aiton, along with other piping contractors, refused to supply design expertise without the guaranteed involvement in any subsequent hardware supply. A Joint Venture, the BPA-JV was formed between Babcocks, PED and Aiton. Eventually a contract worth £100 million was negotiated, including a contract to Whessoe Technical Computing Systems, subsequently worth £10 million, for the provision of a Computer Aided Engineering and Management System (CAEMS) to control the design and quality systems from design phase through manufacture and construction.

In 1968 and 1969 respectively two more precision tool companies were added to the fold with the acquisition of Morgan Brace of Glamorgan and Malone Precision Tool Co, of Essex both of which complemented the Express Tool Co. purchased previously.

There was a determination to see Whessoe continue as a major force in the heavy engineering world. To reinforce this an additional new office block was built, allowing for the increased design and engineering functions for exchangers, nuclear and heavy pressure vessels.

The new office brought with it some stricter controls on personnel with a previously unheard of clocking-in system for general staff, a ban on all overtime unless specifically authorized, but a bit of light relief with the granting of four weeks' annual holiday for all staff. The Works at that time being on two weeks' annual holiday.

By the end of 1969, under the leadership of Michael Noone O.B.E, who had been appointed Group Chief Executive, the Whessoe Group had grown from a Darlington based company with 2,000 employees to an International Group with 6,000 employees and had manufacturing facilities at eight locations in the U.K. and six overseas. To control this engineering empire the Divisional structure set-up in earlier years was re-organized to form five Sub-Groups each with a number of Divisions and/or subsidiary companies.

Heavy Eng. Sub-Group

Whessoe Ireland, Whessoe Stockton, Fabrication Div., Construction Div., Whessoe Nigeria.

Light Eng. Sub-Group

Light Products Div., Liquid Trans. Systems, Plastics Div., Whessoe Calais

General Eng. Sub-Group

Whessoe Projects Eng., Engineering Div., Research & Dev. Div.

Precision Eng. Sub-Group

Express Tools, Morgan & Brace, Malone Tools

Aiton Sub-Group

Pipework Projects, Process Plant Div., Aiton Chemineer Div., Australia, Canada.

The decade was coming to a close with Whessoe being, to all outward appearances, a forceful and commercially strong company and a leader in the international field of engineering.

There had been problems, however, in that several large, long- term contracts coming to completion were not showing the profitability envisaged. With steadily deteriorating market conditions and penal interest rates on loans for any long-term funding operation threatening to exceed likely profit margins, questions were being asked at Main Board level about the long-term prospects and the direction the Group was taking. Mainly, though, there were doubts about the ability of the top executive management to control the now extensive group of companies with its many diverse activities.

10

The Nineteen Seventies

By early 1970 a shortage of short-term contracts, which would normally have generated reasonably quick profit returns to help in the long-term funding of major contracts had exacerbated the Group's problems. Expensive short-term borrowings had to be used to find the working capital. As a result the Group recorded a loss in the 1969/1970 Annual Report which was the first time since becoming a Public Company fifty years previously.

This loss inevitably stressed the need for a review of the Group and its management style. Resulting from this, Michael Noone, who had served the Company for thirty-six years, the last seven as Chief Executive, relinquished his position and resigned from the Board with the loss to the engineering world of a very strong and charismatic character known world-wide for his engineering prowess.

At this same time John H. Lord, who had been the Group chairman for nine years, resigned after attaining the age of seventy and Lord Erroll of Hale took over as the new Chairman. Lord Erroll had joined the Whessoe Board in 1965 following his period of service with the government as both Minister of the Board of Trade and Minister for Power. He had been Deputy Chairman since 1967 and was the logical successor. (As Frederick Erroll M.P. he of course officially opened the new Whessoe welding shop in 1963.)

His first task was to set up a Cost Reduction Committee under Reg Slater, the Production Director and acting Group Chief Executive. The committee was charged with examining the entire cost structure of the Group and achieving economies wherever possible, with the object of providing a new, lean and efficient organization capable of meeting competition in the world markets.

Rationalization and surgery were essential. The Plastics Division, which had been having problems for some time, was closed. Similarly, Liquid Transfer Systems, a small outlet acquired previously, failed to meet its profit promises and was merged with Light Products, under one management, it formed Whessoe Systems and Controls, which better described the activities carried out by the Light Engineering enterprise.

In September 1970 a new Group Chief Executive, Mr. W. Smart, was appointed from outside the Group with the aim of bringing more business sense into the executive management. Reorganization of the Group structure was at the top of his priority list. The late Sixties Sub-Group organization was overturned and three separate Divisions created, Heavy Engineering, Light Engineering and Aiton.

The Heavy Engineering Division was formed from the merging of Whessoe Ltd. (Darlington Works and Offices), Whessoe Stockton Works, Whessoe Project Engineering Ltd. and Econotherm (U.K.) the Furnace subsidiary. Ron Bishop, the General Manager of R. & D. was appointed Technical Director reporting directly to Bill Smart.

Further cost saving measures were still necessary. In later months a redundancy programme was introduced at Darlington, Stockton and Aiton, totalling almost 500 redundancies from Works and Staff. This was a first time measure for Whessoe and one which caused considerable unrest amongst the labour force, both in the Works and on the sites.

Industrial relations problems at Whessoe had generally been better than average across site and Works activities. Basically, because, despite the size of the Group, there still existed more of a 'Family Company' relationship between Management and Trade Unions even considering the increase in militancy in the unions since the war. There had always been demarcation lines between individual trades, even within their own unions, but with the full work loads of the 1950s and 60s there was little cause for concern, as there was work for everyone despite some inevitable overmanning.

With the market problems of the 1970s, however, the scarcity of work brought about the unrest mentioned earlier, particularly in the site construction field. In principle, site construction crews were drawn, in the main, from local labour and consideration had always to be given to particular labour traits of the area in order to achieve a reasonable relationship.

On many large construction sites the higher levels of manning necessary to maintain completion dates required that labour be brought in from all over the country with consequent disagreement on wage levels and union demarcation rules. Small disputes quickly spread until whole sites would be shut down over relatively minor matters such as the allocation of overtime, overtime rates of payment and demarcation problems. In the early 1970s laggers and insulators argued about who did sheetmetal working activities and many thousands of man-hours were lost due to these arguments.

Other major disputes erupted about what constituted a pipe or a tube. Was it to be fitted by a plumber or a pipe-fitter? Was a plater allowed to tack weld when setting up a job or had it to be a welder, despite their being in the same union?

The 1970s proved to be a decade of industrial unrest starting with an all out industry strike in Ireland affecting Whessoe (I) Ltd. The pipe-fitter/plumber dispute hit Aiton hard on their sites and the lagger/ insulator problems affected all trades on nearly all sites.

The North Sea fabrication work at Dock Point was not left out of these troubles as all the labour at that time was drawn from other construction sites and they brought the national problems with them. This was further exacerbated by methods of payment to the labour at Laing's Off-shore yard at Graythorpe across the river. They were producing large drilling platforms for the B.P. Forties Field in the North Sea, much of which had been sub-contracted to Whessoe at Dock Point. Completion on time has always been the most critical part of an Off-shore contract.

Delay in floating out large components could hold up the ocean going barges and heavy lift cranes which were reserved on phenomenal daily hire rates. A few weeks delay could cost the oil companies millions. The Graythorpe yard, to overcome this problem, promised grossly exaggerated completion bonuses to the labour if the contract went out on time, sometimes of the order of £3,000 per man. Bearing in mind that construction and sub- contractor crews numbered up to a thousand men at that time the cost was enormous. Once this method of payment had been established other Off-shore yard labour demanded similar treatment. The smaller companies could not afford this and so completion bonuses became self defeating—especially if the oil companies refused to contribute towards this payment. If payment was refused go-slows and wild-cat stoppages abounded creating havoc with time-tables and costs.

These problems continued for several years. In the North-East during the mid-seventies an enormous chemical complex was being developed at Seal Sands on the river Tees. This site had an unfortunate reputation for industrial problems because of the mix of different unions and trades. Whessoe suffered badly in financial terms because of problems with the Phillips/Simchem project being fabricated and constructed by them. One and two day strikes crippled the erection sequences and onerous contract conditions involving penalty payments turned an otherwise good project into a financial burden and a drain on the resources of the Company.

In parallel with much of this, coal miners with deep-seated industrial problems called and escalated national strikes at the pits with the consequent shortage of fuel for the power stations and rationing of electricity supplies across the country.

In December 1973 the government declared a National Energy Crisis and all manufacturing industry, other than those engaged on North Sea development work, were reduced to a three day working week. The Whessoe Darlington and Stockton Works worked only on Monday, Tuesday and Wednesday, work in offices and Works being allowed on other days only if electricity was not used for heating or lighting. This crisis of course hit domestic users as well as industry but not with the same financial impact.

This industrial unrest, like most strikes, did more harm to the industry and its labour force than good. Whessoe, like many other fabricators, had to look again at the effects of work shortage and financial losses. The new organization had engendered more efficient working practices within the Group and, despite the labour problems, by 1975 was back on a profitable basis, however tenuous.

In that particular year much of the recorded profit was made by Heavy Engineering although it was generally due to the completion of several long term contracts without, regrettably, subsequent follow on contracts. So, despite the reputed profit, it proved necessary to issue advance notices of redundancy at both the Darlington and Stockton works.

In addition cuts in public expenditure programmes in the Nationalised Electricity and Steel Industry delayed further nuclear work and steelwork plant contracts, with concern spreading about the possible abandonment of future nuclear power station projects.

In August 1975, 450 staff and works personnel were made redundant at Whessoe, part of the first step in the reversal of the nation's full employment policy and the start of what is today almost a fact of life— uncertain work prospects.

Despite this, all was not doom and gloom, Light Engineering and Aiton were still picking up work on a profitable basis and the 1970s as a whole saw a considerable increase in the heat exchanger market and in Whessoe's share of that market.

To cope with the increase, the heat exchanger thermal and mechanical designers and draughtsmen were brought together to form the Heat Exchanger Department under Ted Saunders. Previously they had been part of individual engineering departments and could be called upon to do work other than heat exchangers.

As chemical and refinery plants became larger and more complex, the design and material selection for heat exchanger manufacture became more complicated. Materials to withstand extremes of temperature and pressure as well as corrosive gases and fluids demanded modifications to chemical compositions which did not necessarily lend themselves to good weldability. Consequently, material selection became a more vital part of design.

The process and design specifications laid down by the customer became quite extensive and the interpretation of these specifications and the selection of suitable materials was necessary before any final detailed designs could be established.

It was in this area that my earlier experience on the shop floor and the estimating department stood me in good stead. Ted Saunders offered me the position of Projects Engineer, a new situation that became available and one which would obviously be of great job interest with good possibilities of further advancement. Again, I was very fortunate to be working for some one who went out of his way to advance his staff, provided they showed enough interest and initiative.

To remain competitive, designs, materials and methods of manufacture had to be investigated and standardized as much as possible. But the initial important requirement was to get the thermal design right to give the necessary performance with the minimum surface area of tubing, which is generally the major cost item of an exchanger.

Whessoe had been manufacturing exchangers since 1946, originally in ones or twos and of small diameter. By the 1970s orders were being based on plants requiring up to 100 exchangers and manual calculations for both thermal and mechanical designs proved inadequate to cope with the influx of work.

To support the department's own thermal design methods and to keep abreast of the latest heat transfer and fluid flow data Whessoe became members of H.T.F.S. (Heat Transfer and Fluid Flow Service) of Harwell and of H.T.R.I. (Heat Transfer Research Incorporated) of the U.S.A. These organizations provided essential data based on operational testing and were supported by more than 100 companies from various countries. Whessoe were the only wholly British fabricator to have full membership.

The increase in exchanger size to meet new plant capacities had led to flow-induced acoustic and tube vibration which in some cases could destroy an exchanger in a matter of hours. Whessoe made a study of this problem and developed computer programs so that all thermal designs were given a rigorous vibration analysis.

In conjunction with the Whessoe Technical computer department a comprehensive computer program called HERMES (Heat Exchanger Rating and Mechanical Engineering Service) was developed which incorporated a previously developed mechanical design program HECATE (Heat Exchanger Computerised Aid to Engineering). These combined programs offered a full thermal and mechanical design service and the output provided detailed specification sheets, Bills of Materials and

High integrity T.I.G. welding of tube ends into a heat exchanger double tubesheet assembly.

estimating data and were so refined that they gave Whessoe an edge against U.K. competitors in particular. Eventually the service was offered to industry as a separate function, providing thermal and/or mechanical designs, with or without guarantees, from the customer's own process data or alternatively gave design appraisal of fully established designs by others.

As Whessoe's reputation grew, inquiries came in from overseas sources which inevitably meant visits to their offices, to discuss designs and prices, personal contact being essential if we were to maintain and develop these markets. As the Senior Projects Engineer responsible for interpretation of customer's requirements and an overall understanding of Whessoe's offer, I found myself once again working away for Whessoe. In most cases I travelled as part of a team, comprising either a thermal designer, a discipline I was not qualified to deal with, or a senior estimator if detailed costing adjustments had to be made. Over a period of years we obtained work for Algeria, America, Canada, Cyprus, Germany, Holland, Italy, Kenya, Libya, Poland, Qatar, South Africa, Spain and Yugoslavia.

A mixed-alloy 78"/96 kettle-type exchanger with a 'U' tube bundle designed and built for Qatar Petroleum.

Two visits, in particular, I recall with pleasure. One was a visit to Toronto, Canada, when we were called upon to attend a "two hour" meeting to discuss mechanical design and welding problems associated with 13 per cent chrome iron material to be used in some exchangers for a Deuterium Oxide (Heavy Water) plant for part of the Canadian CANDU nuclear programme. I went accompanied by Chris Reeks a senior Works welding engineer, a very agreeable companion. We travelled on one of the first Boeing 747 Jumbo jets, directly to Toronto. The plane was less than half full and the service from the cabin staff, therefore, was excellent, plus we had the freedom to occupy a whole row of seats and sleep if so desired. During one of these periods Chris had a visit to the flight deck which I missed, much to my chagrin.

It was our first visit to Canada and we were not disappointed. The weather was glorious, the food almost too much but, most importantly, we were successful in our technical meeting and obtained an order for 17 exchangers against considerable Canadian and American competition.

As we were leaving on the next day's flight we didn't have much time for sightseeing but did bump into the flight crew of the aircraft we came over on in a local pub. We found that we were travelling back on the same flight again and over a drink or two obtained a promise for me to visit the flight deck during the trip home, which was a most interesting experience at that time for an engineer.

The one and only disappointment on the trip was that there was a national transport strike on at the time of our visit and we didn't have an opportunity to visit Niagara Falls.

The other visit which stands out in my mind was one to Rome a few years later when we were competing for a series of heat exchangers for a plant in Colombia. At the time our most serious competition was coming from Italian fabricators, basically because their government was subsidizing steel production to such an extent that in general their selling prices were less than the U.K. material cost element which, in itself, represented about 50 per cent of our total exchanger price.

Our refined thermal designs had provided surface areas and overall designs that would normally have produced competitive prices against normal competition. It was, however, our overall design and guarantees that interested the Italian Construction company who were installing the plant in Colombia.

Three of us spent four days in Rome going through design details and prices. The other two members of the team were Peter Johnson, our London sales engineer and Ray Rocket who was now the senior heat exchanger estimator.

The thing that remains with me was the Englishman's total disregard for other languages. There were five buyers and engineers at each meeting, two Italian, one Egyptian, one west African and a Frenchman. Each spoke fluent English and Italian and we of course, spoke only English. Nevertheless, the meetings were very agreeable and, although our prices were not the lowest, after some negotiation we won the contract.

In the evening we ate at local restaurants and on one occasion the three of us were serenaded by a musical trio and when they realized we were English sang one or two typically English ballads. They asked for our own requests and by the late evening the trio and most of the restaurant were singing the *Lambton Worm* and other Geordie ditties and a good time was had by all.

On our last day we found time to visit the Colosseum, Pantheon and St. Peter's Basilica. The latter I found to be a most awe inspiring sight and a highlight to the visit.

By this time the reader should have noted that my views on working away for Whessoe had changed somewhat from those earlier days, but so had the conditions. Good first class hotels and Club class air travel are a far cry from the Sailors' hostel at Grangemouth.

The heat exchanger market continued to flourish and through the period we manufactured over 2,000 individual exchangers including some of the largest units ever manufactured with lengths up to 72 ft. and diameters of 10 ft. and more.

By 1973 the Dock Point site (Teesside) had been extensively developed for the fabrication of large constructions, structural components and complex Service modules for Off-shore platforms.

The 18 acre site had a 2,000 ft. frontage to the River Tees, which was 500 ft. wide at that point. A new 100 ft. wide loading out platform had been installed at the Point, capable of accommodating sea-going barges and taking loads of 2,000 tons.

Load bearing concrete covering an area of 200,000 sq. ft. had been laid and a new Goliath crane with a 200 ft. span and lifting capacity of 100 tons. installed. Covered fabrication shops and new offices were available making the site more suited to meet the requirements of heavy constructional engineering.

As North Sea exploration developed it became apparent that Dock Point could become a further vital part of Whessoe's heavy engineering capability with a long term future. Competition was not as fierce as land based product lines and there was a place for Whessoe's acknowledged high quality workmanship.

In 1975/6 the Board invested significant sums and purchased or leased more land to extend the site to 31 acres with more fabrication shops and concrete. A decision that was justified in later years, particularly in the 1980s, despite continued labour problems over the first few years.

This 300-foot diameter floating roof storage tank was the largest tank of its kind in Europe. It was designed and built by Whessoe for Fina/Total Oil GB Ltd. for their Lindsay Oil Refinery at Killingholme.

For the next three years to 1978, concentration on better contract management and financial control brought a steady increase in Group profits and a reduction in short-term borrowings. A tight rein continued to be kept on expenditure and staff and labour recruitment. By 1976 the average number of Group employees had fallen from a peak of 6,000 to 4,250.

The Board, in reviewing the expansion of Heavy Engineering, also took a detailed look at Precision Engineering and decided that future development in the Precision Engineering field was not appropriate for Whessoe. They concluded the sale of Express Tools, Morgan and Brace and Malone Engineering to the Rodd Engineering Co. of Shepperton, Middlesex. The funds released from the sale were to be used more profitably in the main stream of Heavy Engineering.

During these three years a £2 million contract was won by the Darlington Works for a number of large 250 feet diameter floating roof tanks for SHELL at Anglesey, North Wales. They provided storage capacity for 4.5 million barrels of crude oil and utilized 13,000 tons of steel plate. Later in the year Lindsey Oil Refinery placed an order for a 300 feet diameter oil storage tank, the largest tank of its kind in Britain with a storage capacity of 30 million gallons.

Within the same period, Whessoe Systems and Controls marketed a new Liquid Level Gauge for wine storage and also won a large contract for gauging equipment for a new refinery at Tabriz, Iran.

Whessoe Ireland secured a major contract for a sugar silo with a capacity of 30,000 tons, the largest in Ireland and one of the largest in the world.

Aiton did well with an order for the design, supply and fabrication of a pipework system for Calgary Generating Station in Alberta, Canada. More significantly they obtained a contract valued at £1. million for the design, supply and installation of pipework for the C.E.G.B. Dinorwic Pumped Storage Hydro-Electric Generating Station in Snowdonia, North Wales.

The Dinorwic Project was one of the world's most ambitious schemes for harnessing water. Hydro-electric pumped storage schemes were the only ones that had shown sufficient promise to be adopted for large scale energy storage and the subsequent generation and distribution of electricity.

The scheme operates by pumping water to a higher level using surplus night-time electricity and then using the stored potential energy in the water to generate electricity at peak periods during the day. After driving the turbines the water is later pumped back to the upper reservoir and used over and over again on a daily basis.

Two natural lakes were chosen for these upper and lower reservoirs, an enlarged lake called the Llyn Peris reservoir was at the lower end and a further enlarged lake called the Marchlyn Mawr reservoir at the upper end. They have a vertical separation of 500 metres over an overall run length of 3,200 metres.

The Power House or Turbine Hall containing six reversible pumped turbines each capable of generating 300 MW, was excavated from within the bowels of the existing slate mountain. Being twice the length of a football pitch and as high as a sixteen storey building it was believed to be the biggest man-made cavern in Europe.

Dinorwic also has the fastest response time of any pumped storage station in the world and in an emergency can contribute 1,800 megawatts

An impression of the size of the excavations in the bowels of Snowdonia during the building of the Dinorwic hydro-electric power station. It is the biggest man-made cavern in Europe.

of electricity to the National Grid in ten seconds, using 1,400 million gallons of water. It became known as the ten second Wonder of the World and has been described as the construction feat of the twentieth century.

The original scheme was built at a cost of £425 million and the Aiton's contract for £1 million of pipework in the Turbine Hall seems an insignificant amount in comparison but the true value to the Whessoe Group at that time was inestimable as it led directly to Whessoe's involvement in a complete new sphere of operations.

The design of the system called for the drilling and blasting of 16 kilometres of tunnelling up to 10 metres diameter, down through the mountain. It was necessary to smooth line these tunnels using over 400,000 cubic metres of concrete. Nearer to the Turbine Hall the

Whessoe's high pressure tunnel liners moving along access tunnels within the mountain.

hydraulic tunnels were steel lined to form a tightly toleranced approach to the steel penstocks leading to the main inlet valves and discharge tubes.

It was here that Whessoe's experience in high quality, tight toleranced pressure vessels came into its own. Orders were eventually received for the supply and installation of over £7 million worth of cylindrical steel lining sections, including the large steel intermediate penstock assemblies. It involved the shop fabrication and on-site construction of

Steel tunnel liners being set in position for welding.

the six high pressure and six low pressure tunnel liners. The overall length of one complete high pressure and low pressure line was 220 metres (720 ft.) with diameters ranging up to 4.5m in steel plate up to 80mm (3 in.) thick. Many of the final welding operations were carried out in very cramped conditions several hundreds of feet below ground.

The major civil contractors for the project were M.B.Z (McAlpine, Brand & Zschokke) with Boving & Co. in support. Boving & Co. were eventually to become a joint venture partner with Whessoe in several similar overseas ventures in the 1980s.

With contracts like Dinorwic, Whessoe's reputation continued to grow but its fortunes were forever changing. The heavy engineering industry continued to be somewhat erratic in its work load for the rest of the decade.

Final assembly at Whessoe Stockton works of a 125 ton capacity basic oxygen furnace.

Whessoe Stockton Works, whose main customer had always been the steel processing industry, won several contracts in 1977 for Kilns and Converters, the most notable being two 50 ton Top Blow Rotary Converters for the extraction and smelting of nickel. The contract was valued at £1 million and was completed 11 weeks ahead of schedule for delivery to Indonesia. The U.K. market, however, was foundering with steel mills on short time or closing down altogether. By 1978, although the Group was profitable, Whessoe Stockton was proving to be a liability and was eventually closed down with the loss of 600 jobs. It also had a knock on effect on the Darlington facility and a further 230 jobs were lost there.

Darlington at about that time won £7.5 million of heat exchangers and process columns for Ethylene plants at I.C.I. Wilton and Corpus Christi in Texas, but even these heralded the end of major complexes and heat exchanger and pressure vessel contracts dropped in numbers significantly.

Overseas contractors were becoming more proficient at erecting their own plants, certainly in the more standard materials, and whilst Darlington won a £4 million contract for the design and supply of pre-fabricated tanks for Yugoslavia, the site erection, Whessoe's forte, was lost to Yugoslavian erectors.

Aiton and Light Engineering continued to make steady progress maintaining reasonable profit levels on lesser contracts with quicker turn a-rounds.

The Gas Boards were developing and extending their natural gas storage schemes and Whessoe's undoubted expertise in the design of double skinned cryogenic storage tanks won them several multi-million pound contracts in 1978 for L.N.G. storage at the Isle of Grain, Partington and Avonmouth. This particular expertise continues to be one of Whessoe's major capabilities in the world today.

It is interesting to record, amongst other things, the multiplicity of events that occurred in the last two years of the decade, in particular;

Econotherm U.K. Ltd. was wound up.

Whessoe Heavy Engineering Ltd. was formed, with all the heavy engineering activities of Whessoe Ltd. transferred to that title. Ron Bishop was appointed Group Managing Director.

One of two 50,000 cu.m. capacity double-skinned storage tanks, designed and built for British Gas at their Isle of Grain installation.

Whessoe Projects Engineering Ltd. was also wound up.

Whessoe bought in to British Nuclear Associates (B.N.A.), again with Ron Bishop as a Director, keeping his eye on the nuclear scene.

Claude Spielman our Honorary President died at the age of 89.

A full size replica of the *Rocket*, George Stephenson's famous railway engine, was manufactured for the Science Museum and National Railway Museum to celebrate the 150th Anniversary of the Rainhill Locomotive Trials of 1829, run to determine the most superior type of locomotive that would be used to haul passengers on the Liverpool–Manchester railway service. Whessoe apprentices were asked to design and build the boiler, which although being of similar dimensions to the original had to meet the current stringent pressure vessel design code, BS5500.

The engine is currently on display outside the Royal Albert Hall in London and was the second similar project carried out by Whessoe apprentices, who in 1975 also built the boiler for the replica of *Locomotion No.1*, which runs to this day at Beamish Museum in Northumberland.

In 1979 Costain Construction approached Whessoe with a view to negotiating a merger between the two Groups. At the time Whessoe Directors were of the opinion that, on the grounds of general industrial logic, a merger with Costain could have many long-term advantages and entered into preliminary discussions.

The talks, however, were thwarted by a claim from Qatar Petroleum for damages against Shell Internationale Petroleum Maatschappi NV (S.I.P.M.) and Whessoe following an explosion at a tank farm at Umm Said, Qatar. Shell designed the tanks and Whessoe built them. The claim was strongly contested on the basis that operation of the plant was outside SIPM/Whessoe control and detailed investigations could reveal no design or manufacturing fault, but in view of the claim Costain notified Whessoe that it did not intend to pursue the merger.

The replica of the Rocket *locomotive on display outside the Royal Albert Hall, London. The boiler was designed and built by Whessoe engineering apprentices.*

Litigation took several years and in the end Qatar Petroleum withdrew its claim against both SIPM and Whessoe, but by this time Costain had lost interest.

In the midst of these problems the Engineering Union put a ban on all overtime working across the country and introduced more one and two day strikes. Although Whessoe Group profits were up slightly against previous years it was estimated that this action cost Whessoe over £600,000 in trading profits over the year with further knock-on effects on cash flow, borrowing and interest charges.

What was needed was a shot in the arm to bolster up the core business and produce more activity, thus relieving the tension in the labour force that the series of recent redundancies had caused.

This shot in the arm came in the latter months of 1979 with an order valued at £80 million for the design, fabrication and construction of major components associated with two Advanced Gas Cooled Nuclear Reactor Power Stations to be built at both Heysham and Torness in Scotland. This order came after a total lack of nuclear contracts since the 1960s and even this one was considered to be a holding operation by the government until at such time as a decision could be reached on the future use of Pressure Water Reactors (P.W.R.). If these A.G.R.s had not been placed there could have been a serious loss of skill and expertise amongst the British designers and fabricators. Nevertheless, it was an absolute life saver for Whessoe and the other consortium members.

Each of the two stations were to comprise two 660 MW reactors and Whessoe were to supply the gas-tight steel membrane liners for each of the four pre-stressed concrete pressure vessels which housed the nuclear reactor and boilers, the steel support structures (Diagrids) for the graphite cores and the steel vessels which enclosed and segregated the cores. In addition 32- large steel tubular access penetrations were required which necessitated very precise machining operations.

The award to Whessoe by the Nuclear Power Co. Ltd (N.P.C.) on behalf of the Central Electricity Generating Board (C.E.G.B.) and the South of Scotland Electricity Board (S.S.E.B.) represented the largest single order ever to be received in the Company's history and was to provide a substantial base work load for the Design, Fabrication and Construction departments for several years.

This order linked with a major high pressure pipework contract awarded to Aiton for the same power stations brought the value of Power station orders won by the Whessoe Group in recent months to over £100 million and the Groups gross orders to £230 millions.

11

The Nineteen Eighties

Despite the tremendous fillip the receipt of the A.G.R. order gave to the Group and the degree of activity it aroused within Heavy Engineering and Aiton, it was acknowledged that the Darlington Works would only be involved, to any great degree, with the boilersmith trades. The other bread and butter lines were still affected by the general and continuing depression in process plant demand and the majority of the machining capacity would be under used. As a result of this inactivity and the consequential lack of overhead recovery the Group recorded a significant loss with most of this coming from Heavy Engineering.

This loss, once again, adversely affected cash flow within the Group and borrowings were still high to support the long-term contracts.

It turned out that 1979/1980 was to be a difficult period of delays, transitions and redeployment with the uncertainty of the Qatar claim still hovering and it was inevitable that redundancies and reorganization had to be contemplated.

Within this reorganization the production side of Darlington Works came under the control of Alan Rowley as Director and General Manager of the Nuclear Division and the process plant areas came under Frank Middlemiss the Director and General Manager of the Process Plant Division. Both of them reported directly to Ron Bishop the Managing Director.

Decisions were made at this time to withdraw temporarily from the manufacture of Heat Exchangers, M & J Valves, Shop Built Pressure Vessels and Iron and Steel Equipment, all of which were currently in a minimal workload situation and thus the early release of staff and labour directly associated with these products was possible.

This had personal implications for me, as the Heat Exchanger Projects Engineer, now well established in a middle management role. The cessation of heat exchanger manufacture left my career up in the air but, fortunately for me, Frank Middlemiss was looking for a Contracts Manager to co-ordinate, with a team of engineers, all of the Process Plant Division orders numbering at that time, over one hundred active contracts, many of them major site projects. I was offered the position with immediate promotion to senior management which brought with it a company car and other fringe benefits.

It was in this position that I feel my commercial education was rounded off, a sound business sense being, in my opinion, an essential part of any manager's make-up. Michael Noone the 1960s M.D. was always telling us that we were not in the business to make heat exchangers or nuclear reactors, we were in the business to make money and it was a lesson well learnt.

During this period other changes involved the transposition of the Technical Computer department into a limited company. Whessoe Technical Computer Systems Ltd. (W.T.C.S.) being formed as a subsidiary of W.H.E. Ltd. which, within itself, had now only the two divisions, Nuclear Reactor Divison and Process Plant Division.

The Process Plant Division controlled all products other than nuclear including site work both home and overseas.

The Nuclear Reactor Division basically handled much of the Darlington Works activity which was predominantly the shop fabrication of all the components of the four new A.G.R. reactors for Heysham and Torness.

Two previous Nuclear Power Stations, Hunterston 'B' and Hinkley Point 'B' commissioned in 1976 were making significant contributions to the national grid and indicating generation costs substantially lower than those of contemporary fossil-fired stations. Designs for the current reactors were continuations of the Hunterston and Hinkley stations, but manufacturing techniques were refined so that much more of the project could be carried out under shop condition, thus reducing the man-hours expended on site with all of its climatic and industrial relations problems.

Welding cooling water pipes onto A.G.R. liner panels at the Darlington works.

As an example of this technique the concrete reactor vessels had steel liners which were 20 m diameter × 22 m high and weighed 600 tonnes each. These liners were made in the Darlington Works as sixteen separate panels rolled to an exact radius and had rectangular section cooling water pipes welded to the external surfaces in specially designed jigs which eliminated any distortion due to welding stresses. Under these conditions it was possible to deliver a set of panels to site and within three days all sixteen panels would be erected on prepared foundations and positioned for final site welding.

Similarly, the steel pressure vessels comprising Gas Baffle assembly, Dome, Diagrid and Restraint Tank were all manufactured plate-small and finally assembled and welded in custom-built workshops at Dock Point the Whessoe Offshore facility.

The Gas Baffle assemblies were subjected to 100 per cent radiography and ultrasonic examination before and after stress relief. Upon completion the complete units, each weighing 1,000 tonnes, were moved out of the shop using unique "walking" hydraulic jacks and then transferred to multiwheel trailers and loaded onto sea-going barges for shipment directly to Heysham and Torness coastal sites.

This method proved so efficient that the first complete unit went out exactly on the day planned two and a half years before and successive ones were shipped out ahead of programme. Overall some 400,000 site man-hours were saved by the shop fabrication procedures.

A 450 ton combined lift of the Heysham Nuclear Restraint Tank and Gas-Baffle Cylinder onto its diagrid and support skirt in the Whessoe Offshore purpose built assembly shop.

To complete the fabrication work four sets of reactor roof assemblies which contained the Charge and Control stand-pipes were assembled and welded at Dock Point with the structure so designed that, with external panelling, they formed their own weather proof shops enabling specialized remote controlled orbital welding techniques to be carried

Site assembly of 16 nuclear reactor liner panels by Whessoe construction crews, prior to welding.

out under almost "clean conditions". Each of these units was also moved out on sea-going barges for delivery direct to site.

The Stand-pipes themselves, 406 per reactor, were manufactured in a specially designed workshop at Darlington. Machines were devised to helically coil steel cooling water pipes to fit over the external surface of each Stand-pipe which were then automatically stitch welded to the pipe to provide the carefully calculated heat transfer requirements between the hot Stand-pipe and the cooling medium.

All of the fabrication work on the two contracts went without any serious hitches providing tremendous activity for the heavy engineering facilities at Darlington and Dock Point and supplying the sites with materials exactly to programme. The success was due entirely to careful planning, method study and the co- operation of both labour and staff as closely knit teams, with only one hiccup.

In January 1981, 350 members of the T. & G. W. union walked out of the Darlington Works on unofficial strike due to failure to obtain promises of a significant pay rise from the management. Although the

The very complicated high integrity gas baffle dome showing stand pipe connections being welded in at Whessoe's offshore yard at Middlesbrough, Teesside.

Group recorded a small profit in 1980/1981 the Heavy Engineering Division in fact made a loss due, in the main, to the lack of support from other product lines and the management considered pay rises of the magnitude being requested to be unsupportable at that time. The walk-out effectively brought the workshops to a standstill and eventually the balance of 500 workers were sent home due to lack of work.

Union chiefs recommended a return to work after one week so that further negotiations could take place and the strike was eventually settled after it was accepted by the unions that their claim was unreasonable and a full return to work occurred after a week of inactivity.

Although of relative short duration the strike created significant gaps in the nuclear programme but re-scheduling and extra shift work soon brought the contract back on programme, although at significant cost to the Company and of course to the men, who lost a full week's wage's without any overall benefit. Proving once again the futility of strike action as opposed to sensible negotiation.

There was, however, more to the strike than mere pay increases. The fear of lost jobs as the contracts were concluded without any signs of immediate replacement work was cause for great concern and extra money in the hand now, was quite understandably the only short-term answer the workforce could see.

In the meantime site work went ahead without undue delay and on a very profitable basis so that by 1981/1982 Heavy Engineering was in profit again with A.G.R. providing the bulk of this although Aiton made a considerable contribution with an order book in excess of £100 million. The management were now able to make good their earlier promises to provide substantial pay increases to the workforce but by mid 1982 most of the fabrication work at Darlington was complete and as a result of the overall fall in work load the feared redundancies were announced.

In considering the Company's future a strategic plan was produced which involved the move into new markets and re-entry into old markets as they recovered from the recession. A major component of this strategy was a planned return to the Heat Exchanger business. This product at one time provided a substantial proportion of the Darlington work load.

As explained earlier U.K. manufacturers in recent years were overtaken by overseas competition in a very depressed market exacerbated also by a failure to invest in modern equipment.

The Company had taken advantage of the heavy A.G.R. shop load to withdraw completely, albeit temporarily, from this and other similar markets. It now wished to re-establish itself in this sector based upon its proven design and manufacturing capabilities and hopefully improved productivity and better equipment.

During the period that the Company had been out of these markets, technological changes and innovations had altered manufacturing concepts and there was now widespread use of computer numerically controlled (C.N.C.) machines, plasma torch technology and micro-processor controlled equipment. Investment in this type of equipment was eventually to cost the Group over £5 million.

Apart from re-entering the production market it was decided to endeavour to sell Whessoe's know-how in engineering design and manufacture.

Ron Bishop during recent visits to Mexico had been considering the potential of under developed markets in that country, particularly in the oil related industries. The country had a huge, cheap labour pool but very few skilled engineers and most of the capital plant was being imported.

Whessoe was approached by a Mexican entrepreneur seeking to involve Whessoe in the transfer of technology and the setting up of a Heat Exchanger manufacturing plant in Mexico.

The intention was, through a Joint Venture with Mexican business-men, to set up a green field heat exchanger manufacturing plant in Mexico and for Whessoe engineers to train local labour and engineers in the modern techniques and then run the factory on a joint 50–50 basis.

Before any commitment could be made it was essential that a full market survey was done to establish the long-term business prospects and for that purpose a three man team was sent out to Mexico. The team comprised Ted Saunders, to look at available design and technology, Ken Duffield the Group Financial Controller to investigate commercial and financial aspects of the venture and myself to look at manufacturing and material availability and also industrial relations.

Upon our arrival in Mexico City we were met at the airport by our Mexican contact, who spoke excellent English and turned out to be a Professor of Economics at the City University and an entrepreneur on the side. He was also an hidalgo, a member of the Mexican nobility with considerable sway in the country. The next day we were invited to his home to meet his family but more particularly several senior industrialists who could possibly be of help to us during the visit.

There were actually something like sixty or seventy guests but as the day wore on the numbers dwindled until there were about a dozen left and most of these were executives of construction companies who were able to give us some useful contacts for products other than heat exchangers. Almost two-thirds of Mexico's industrial power was represented at this party. Four brothers of our contact alone, monopolized the glass and steel industry and owned most of Mexico's communications industry including newspapers, as well as a chain of cinemas and radio and television studios.

We had planned a four week tour and appointments had been set up with government ministers and oil and power generation officials.

Due to the lack of professional people in Mexico it was apparent that the majority of senior people had two jobs. All of the meetings with government officials took place in the evenings as they had their own professions to fulfil during the day. I had a meeting with the Minister of Labour at eight o'clock one evening. After two weeks of meetings and discussions it became apparent to us that we were being fed a very rosy picture by these people in an effort to encourage Whessoe to invest both money and technology. Almost half of the contacts were university graduates who had studied under our contact in his role of Professor of Economics and appeared to have some sort of allegiance to him.

We eventually insisted that we make our own contacts and visited senior officials in PEMEX the national petroleum company and in the electric and other power utilities. Talking to engineers there, we got a somewhat different picture.

Although they would welcome the development of local manufacturing facilities they did not consider their overall requirements for new plant to be sufficient to support such an enterprise. They were buying their plant directly from Japan and America at very competitive rates and saw no reason to change.

To get the full picture we next flew down to the green field site destined for the establishment of the proposed factory. It was certainly a wide open site with direct access to a spur line from the main Mexican railway system. It was just outside a small town called Matamoros in the north east corner of Mexico and was my idea of a typical Spaghetti Western Cowboy town complete with tumbleweed and adobe buildings almost on the banks of the Rio Grande. That in itself was an eye opener. At the point of crossing into Texas U.S.A. the Rio Grande was no more than a muddy trickle with access into Brownsville, Texas, by a Bailey bridge.

We stayed the night in Brownsville. Any expatriates coming to work on the proposed plant would need to live there, not Mexico, for very apparent domestic and sanitary reasons.

By this time the venture was looking more and more like a no-go operation. The country itself was financially unstable and during our short stay currency had been devalued three times. Before concluding our visit, however, we decided to investigate another area and we flew to Houston Texas, the commercial centre of the American oil industry and talked to American steel suppliers and banking outlets. If the enterprise was such a viable proposition why weren't the Americans doing it? We learned that tax laws, industrial relations and supply routes were all very tenuous in Mexico and they preferred to sell into Mexico rather that set up manufacturing plants.

The only successful company was Caterpillar Tractors who had single product mass production lines where local unskilled labour could be taught repetitive operations without any real skill being necessary.

Heat exchanger manufacture is a very specialized business and we were now decided that our visit report would not recommend a Whessoe venture into Mexico and we returned home after four weeks of very educational and illuminating discussions.

An interesting diversion from our normal visits was a visit to the National Power Research department in Cuernavaca, 10,000 feet above sea level, a most beautiful area where the British film star Merle Oberon had her home. A biography of Merle recorded that her father, one Henry O'Brien Thompson, was a mechanical engineer from Darlington in the north-east of England and, although I couldn't find any factual evidence, it was most probable that he was employed at one time by Whessoe around the 1920s. Film star production could very well have been another of Whessoe's achievements!

Our final report was accepted by the Whessoe management and other avenues were sought for Whessoe's talents. I discovered later that I was pencilled in for the position of General Manager of the proposed heat exchanger factory which may well have been a very interesting period of my career although I am not so sure my family would have enjoyed it.

Although the Mexican project was a dead duck, Heavy Engineering were having better luck in other areas. Hard on the heels of the successful performance on contracts for tunnel linings and penstocks for the Dinorwic Power Station, the Overseas Division, in collaboration with Boving & Co. Ltd., were awarded a contract valued at £15 million for similar work on the Victoria Dam Project of the Mahaweli Water Authority in Sri Lanka, providing activity over the next three years.

The Victoria Dam and Hydro-Electric Scheme was one of four major dams being built as part of the Sri Lankan Master Plan for Irrigation and Power generation. The Victoria Dam was considered the most beneficial project, being designed to produce 210 MW of electric power in the first phase with the capability of producing a further 210 MW in a later phase. There was also irrigation benefits under the project which was spread over 112,000 acres of undeveloped land and provided for the settlement of some 20,000 families in new agricultural areas.

The project also provided work for 20,000 workers in construction activities and eventually absorbed nearly 100,000 persons in gainful employment.

The major portion of the funding for the project, £113 million, was provided by the British Overseas Aid Programme and the project was

An artist's impression of the completed Victoria Dam and hydro-electric project in Sri Lanka.

to involve the services of over sixteen British companies as Consulting Engineers and Contractors.

The Consulting Engineers were Sir Alexander Gibb & Partners with the main civil contractors being Balfour Beatty Nuttall Joint Venture and Costains with the Hydraulic Equipment being provided by Whessoe/Boving.

Although this account tends to concentrate on the Whessoe effort it is well worthwhile providing some detail of the overall project. The power generation capacity was only one sixth of the Dinorwic Project but the construction of a dam and storage reservoir enhanced the magnitude of the project.

The retaining dam was a masterpiece of design, being a double curvature arch dam, varying in thickness from 25 metres at the foundation to 6 metres at the crest which was 122 metres above the foundation. The crest length was 520 metres and the dam contained 480,000 m³ of concrete. Due to tropical weather conditions it was necessary to add chilled water and flaked ice during the making of the concrete to reduce the possibility

One of the bottom penstock bends being manoeuvered into its final position by Whessoe construction crews.

of thermal cracking. To do this a special water cooling and flaked ice production plant had to be constructed adjacent to the concrete plant.

The Power Station itself was situated 5 kilometres downstream from the dam and unlike the Dinorwic power station was above ground although the foundations were 26 metres below ground.

To carry the water from the dam to the outfalls, adjacent to the power station, a 6.2 metre diameter power tunnel with a length of 5.8 kilometres was bored through water bearing rock. For the greater part of its length the tunnel was lined with concrete nominally 500mm. thick but for geological reasons the last 420 metres of its length was lined with steel plate.

It was this steel lining, along with the penstocks and a fabricated trifurcation which formed the basis of the Whessoe contract. It was considered cheaper to ship flat plate from the U.K. and roll and weld it into circular sections (cans) at site to form the penstocks and tunnel linings than to fabricate in the U.K. before shipping.

The covered rolling mill and fabrication shop that Whessoe set up to produce the fabrications was a model of its kind and provided factory conditions on a very remote site.

*The three 3m diameter penstocks located and set at one of the anchor
points at Victoria Dam.*

The 420 metres of 5.15 metre diameter steel tunnel lining weighing
1,500 tonnes was rolled from 32mm. thick plate. Then came a fabricated
trifurcation 5.15 metres diameter with three 3-metre branches also fabricated from 32mm. plate. The trifurcation was designed to split the
water flow from the main power tunnel to the three penstocks which
fed the turbines inside the Power Station. The trifurcation was the most
complicated component and was designed under license from Escher
Wyss of Zurich who supplied the development co-ordinates to Whessoe
who then carried out the initial fabrication and trial assembly at
Darlington. The data supplied by Escher Wyss was fed into Whessoe's
C.N.C. computer which then produced production tapes for the
Hancommander C.N.C. burning machine. The tape data instructed
the machine to powder burn the back marks for inspection checking,
the conical bend lines for the roll operation, the great circle lines for
the plater and of course the torch path. After the burning operation had
been completed the plates were transferred directly to the rolls for
forming and then trial erected prior to shipment.

View of the trifurcation being transported into its final position following welding and stress relief in the Whessoe on-site workshop.

On site in Sri Lanka the trifurcation, weighing 65 tonnes was re-erected and welded, radiographed and then lagged for local stress relief before being installed at the power station end of the tunnel.

To complete the initial fabrication contract three 3-metre diameter penstocks each 190 metres long were fabricated from 22mm. and 32mm. plate.

As this initial fabrication was being completed a further contract was placed with Whessoe by Balfour Beatty Nuttall for the supply of two low level outlets each consisting of an inlet transition 5.15 m diameter to 4.1 m × 4.1 m square, a 4.1 m square to 4.1 m diameter transition and a 4.1 m diameter circular lining with lobster back bends.

When all of the elements of the tunnel linings and penstocks were completed in the workshops they were then hauled to the tunnels on specially adapted tractors and trailers installed and welded in situ.

The Boving part of the Joint Venture was responsible for the rest of the hydraulic equipment comprising—eight Spillway Gates and three 3-metre diameter Portal Butterfly Valves. They also supplied three Travelling Cranes, two Electric Cranes and one Mobile Crane.

The large proportion of the Boving work was manufactured in the U.K. but Whessoe/Boving were jointly responsible for the site erection and commissioning of all the mechanical equipment as well as the erection of the Low Level Outlets for Balfour Beatty Nuttall.

The trifurcation shown being welded into the three penstocks and valve house.

The work at Victoria started in 1980 and by the end of 1983 the Whessoe/Boving operation was almost complete in accordance with the original programme, having installed over 3,000 tonnes of steelwork.

The Victoria Project was Whessoe's first major involvement overseas in a hydro-electric project and valuable experience was gained which enabled them to pursue other similar projects.

Almost before the dust had settled on the Victoria Dam contract in 1984, Whessoe won another major overseas hydro-electric power project in Indonesia.

The Mrica Hydro-Electric Power Project was to be constructed in Java for P.L.N. the Indonesian Electric Supply Authority and it included Indonesia's largest earth filled dam which would harness the power of the Serayu river in Central Java and would generate 180 MW of electricity as well as contributing to the overall irrigation programme.

The Project was funded from British and Swedish sources and was to make a major contribution to the availability of electric power in Java.

Two bifurcations for the Indonesian hydro-electric scheme at Mrica, during trial erection at the Darlington works. The fabrication on the left comprises a 7.5m diameter inlet with 6.1m and 4.3m outlets.

One of the main advantages to British contractors on this sort of project is the fact that payment for completed work is almost guaranteed as the funding is overseen by the British Overseas Development Agency (O.D.A.) and supported by the Export Credits Guarantee Department (E.C.G.D.).

The overall contract was awarded to SABCON an Anglo-Swedish consortium comprising Skanska, A.S.E.A. and Balfour Beatty Construction, Boving & Co. were nominated mechanical contractors for the project and Whessoe were asked by them to supply the Tunnel Linings and a manifold with two bifurcations.

The project was very similar to that in Sri Lanka with a Dam and a Power Station with three turbines.

The earth filled dam was sited some 200 metres above sea level with power intakes upstream and generation facilities downstream.

To construct the Dam it was first necessary to divert the river away from its current route and this was done by cutting two diversion tunnels in the left bank clear of the proposed Dam site.

Tunnel No. 1 served exclusively for diversion purposes and was subsequently permanently sealed with a concrete plug.

A 7.5m lobster back section of the steel tunnel lining en-route for final location in the power tunnel at Mrica.

Tunnel No. 2 served both for diversion purposes and for subsequent conveyance of water from the power intake to the Power Station.

Both tunnels having an internal diameter of 8.8 m were concrete lined but Tunnel No. 2 was reduced down to 7.5 m diameter and lined with 27mm. thick steel plate. It was this steel lining that Whessoe manufactured from British steel plate, in much the same way as they did in Sri Lanka, using a purpose built site workshop.

The Mrica Project was constructed in two phases. In the first phase the lining was rolled and welded and installed in the tunnel for *in situ* welding and was eventually connected to a vertical dropshaft.

The 80 degree lobster back bend and the two bifurcations were again manufactured plate small in Whessoe's Darlington Works, shipped to site, re-assembled and welded before installation in an open cut trench excavation.

The installation of the tunnel linings and the manufacture of the bend and bifurcations, completed in 1986 formed this first and major phase of what proved to be one of Whessoe's most successful overseas contracts.

The second phase occurred during the low water season of 1988 after completion of the Dam. The connection to the vertical dropshaft

Bottom bend section being manoeuvered into position at Mrica.

and from there to the Power Station via the 80 degree bend and the manifold with the two bifurcations which were then embedded in concrete, was completed during a return to site in 1988.

Encouraged by their continuing success on hydro-electric and irrigation schemes the Overseas Division of Whessoe, against very strong competition, tendered for and were awarded the main contract for the Refurbishment and Rehabilitation of the Sukkur Barrage situated on the River Indus in Pakistan.

The Sukkur Barrage is the largest irrigation scheme of its kind in the world. Originally known as the Lloyd Barrage it is 225 miles north east of Karachi in the Province of Sind. It feeds 6,473 miles of canals to irrigate over 12,000 square miles of cultivated land, equal to one quarter the area of England, through a series of channels, with a total length of 47,000 miles. Work originally commenced in 1923 and the Barrage was opened in 1932.

The Barrage itself comprises 66 spans, each 60 feet wide, stretching a distance of 1¼ kilometres across the Indus. A single steel gate is set in each span each weighing 40 tonnes and these control the river flow.

Seven canals are fed from the Head Pond upstream of the Barrage, four on the left bank and three on the right. These are controlled by a total of 55 Head Regulator Gates, each comprising a three tier system where each gate can be operated independently.

In view of the economic importance of the Barrage to the Province of Sind and following the collapse of a river gate in 1982, the Government of Sind initiated immediate action to strengthen all the existing gates. At the same time they undertook a longer-term programme to rehabilitate the whole Barrage, including the replacement of the 66 Barrage Gates currently in operation and the centre tier of all the 55 Regulator Gates. Rehabilitation of the overhead operating gear was also planned along with completely new electrical, telecommunication and computer systems plus the design and construction of a small but fully equipped workshop for the Barrage personnel.

The whole of this work was included in the scope of the Whessoe contract at a total value of £14 million, funded by the Government of Sind and the U.K. Overseas Development Association (O.D.A.).

The overall contract was planned for completion in 1992, a period of six years' activity. This period was dictated, to a major extent, by the river flow. The Barrage Gates could only be replaced in a working season of mid-October to mid-April. The Head Regulator Gates could only be replaced in a two week period in January when the Barrage Gates were opened for maintenance and the Head Pond fell to a lower level than the canals, thus allowing access to the Regulator Gates.

The main fabrication and installation work was of course to be done in Pakistan and one of the contract conditions was that Whessoe, as

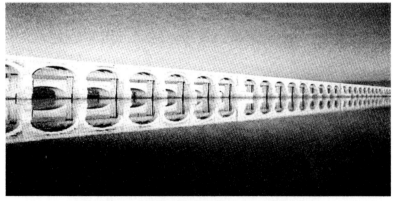

Overall view of the Sukkur Barrage, 1.5km long.
(Photo courtesy Sir M. MacDonald & Partners.)

Installation in the Barrage of a fabricated gate measuring 19m × 8m and weighing 50 tons.

main contractor, had to take on board a Joint Venture partner. A Pakistan Company, DESCON, was selected as an associate on the Project.

The intention was that eventually, as the Pakistani engineers became sufficiently proficient they would take over the responsibility of Project Management. In the event this did not occur and the Whessoe engineers remained on site until completion in 1992.

The whole Project was planned and managed by Whessoe using Pakistani labour with a minimum of Whessoe expatriate engineers to supervise the day to day activities. Work commenced in August 1986 with the erection of a fabrication shop for the gates, a shot-blast and a paint shop, stores, offices and a labour camp. Construction work started in the November of that year using steel shipped from England.

New gates were made in three sections. The sections were welded by local craftsmen following rigorous trade tests and all welds were subjected to radiography and magnetic crack detection tests. Upon completion they were moved to the shot-blast and paint shops and given a single ½mm. thick coat of a special paint applied hot by airless spray. They were then bolted together using 1,400 bolts per gate, all torqued up to the calculated loading.

Prior to installation of the new gates all the existing hoist ropes were tested ultrasonically and found to be defective and were replaced.

To install the gates, a dummy Radial gate on a special pontoon was sealed against the Barrage piers so that the old gate could be removed without disturbing the operation of the Barrage. The old gates were taken away and stored.

The overall project was controlled both commercially and technically from the Head Office in Darlington but they had very little involvement in the fabrication work. The Welding Services Unit of The Group's Research and Development Division were, however, responsible for detailing the fabrication method for the Barrage Gates. Prior to manufacturing the gates in Pakistan any problems which could arise were considered in detail and solved.

A potential problem envisaged with such a large structure was distortion during fabrication, a problem which could be very difficult to rectify at site.

For this contract, what must be one of the largest ever welding test plates, in the form of a full sized section of the gate most likely to distort, was manufactured in a carefully controlled manner. As welding progressed any distortion was measured using highly accurate lasers and theodolites. This work gave all the necessary data to overcome any problems and ensure the trouble- free and on-schedule completion of the project.

So successful was the project that apart from the financial returns, Whessoe were highly complimented both by the Government of Sind and the British Government's Overseas Department which boded well for future work of that type. The final bit of icing on the cake being the award of the M.B.E. for Services to Industry to Brian Voke who had been the original Site Manager and subsequent Project Manager through out the duration of the contract.

Whilst all this overseas activity was going on the rest of the Group Companies, although not at full stretch were supplying a multiplicity of products to almost all areas of industry.

Starting in 1980 Aiton supplied two Desalination Plants for the B.P. Magnus Oil Field. They also designed, supplied and installed all the Low Pressure pipework, compressors, pumps, tanks and heat exchangers for the C.E.G.B. Drax power station at Selby Yorkshire. The Drax contract, which involved the building of three 660 MW coal-fired units, saw the end of the U.K.'s fossil-fired power station programme.

The next power stations were the Nuclear Stations at Heysham and Torness where Aiton was awarded the contract for the High Pressure pipework valued at £20 million. In the same period Aiton (Australia) won a contract for the Bayswater and Mont Piper Power Stations, again valued at £20 million, whilst still in the process of completing a £3.75 million contract for Japan. Aiton (Canada) were also awarded the pipework for the Nova Scotia Power Station valued at £2.75 million, a truly remarkable period for Aiton's turnover and contribution to the Group.

During the 1980s Aiton, as main contractors, designed and supplied the pipework for thirteen Power Stations of varying magnitude through

Four 9,000 gallon desalination plants supplied by Aiton of Derby to the first two BP Forties Field oil platforms in the North Sea.

either their main works at Derby or their Australian and Canadian subsidiaries.

Although Aiton's impressive record for the last twenty years had been based around Power Station work they became well known for unusual contracts, two in particular being a Desalination Plant in a geothermal area 14,000 feet up in the Andes and a small unit designed and supplied to a Fijian Island.

This last one, to my mind, is a good example of the flexibility of Aiton's engineers. The specification required that no electric power was to be used and the fuel supply was coconut husks. Aiton modified

H.P. and L.P. steam pipework designed and installed by Aiton of Derby at the 690 Mw power plant at Hoddisdon, Hertfordshire.

a tar boiler and supplied a hand operated sea water pump and an air cooled condenser.

The plant was capable of being operated by one man and was entirely self contained. The Fijian Government expected that further plants would be required after the first 200 gals./day unit was installed. We can only assume that the manual labour necessary to feed the fuel and operate the pump was not considered to be justified as Aiton never received another order; clearly anything more sophisticated would have increased the capital cost way above the £10,000 of the simple plant and beyond the resources of the local populace.

In this same period of the 1980s Whessoe Heavy Engineering at Darlington designed and supplied Tubular Nodes for an offshore jacket to Phillips Petroleum. Individual nodes weighed up to 80 tonnes and were made from steel plate up to 120mm. thick.

The Massive Nitric acid vessel 4.5m diameter × 38m long weighing 180 tons, being transported from Whessoe's Darlington works to the Hartlepool docks, Teesside. This was the largest vessel ever to come out of the Whessoe works in one piece.

They designed and built a Nitric Acid Vessel measuring 5.43 m diameter × 38.15 m long and weighing 180 tonnes, the largest vessel to be moved by road in the U.K. and most certainly the largest vessel to come out of the Darlington Works in one piece.

They built Condensers for Russia, Skid-Mounted heat exchangers for Abu Dhabi, and an Hyperbaric Living chamber for the deep diving ship H.M.S *Challenger* and a Submarine Escape Test Facility for the Admiralty Marine Technology Establishment. These latter two contracts being of extremely high integrity for Safety of Life situations.

The fields of pressure storage spheres, storage tanks, both standard and cryogenic, were also well represented, plus a £1 million order for eight pressure vessels to be installed in the St. Fergus Oil Terminal in Scotland. Two of the vessels had a design pressure of 115 bar.g and a design temperature range of plus 40°C to minus 54°C necessitating shell thicknesses of 100mm. in carbon manganese steel.

Last but by no means least was a contract for ten Irradiated Fuel flasks to be used for the transportation within the U.K. of radioactive fuel elements between various nuclear power stations and the Sellafield nuclear re-processing plant in Cumbria.

Two low temperature condensers being prepared for shipment to the Gulf of Ob, Russia.

Four crude oil storage spheres, designed and built for Norpipe
Petroleum at Seal Sands, Teesside. At 23.9m (78 ft. 6 in.) diameter they
were Britain's largest spherical pressure vessels.

Each flask started as a hollow forged body weighing 68 tonnes and
a separate lid forging weighing 9 tonnes. It passed through a complex
sequence of stainless steel cladding and C.N.C. controlled machining
operations which reduced the body to 45 tonnes and the lid to 6 tonnes.

At this stage the sides and corners were hollowed out into cavities
which later contained boro silicone resin as a radiation shield.

Having reduced the forgings in this matter the body was built up
again by partly filling the cavities with Triton thermal insulation and
cover plates then closing them off with Tee section fins which control
the temperature of the flask and contents whilst in service. The resin
was then poured into cavities remaining underneath the fins.

High pressure steel storage vessels, 12 ft. diameter × 244 ft. long,
designed and supplied by Whessoe to the British Gas
Corporation at Grimsby.

At all stages the accuracy of machining and fitment was of the
highest order and the fin welding was maintained within close tolerances
by specially developed electronic controls.

After pressure and leak testing the flask was shot blasted and a high
quality paint finish applied.

Several larger cylindrical flasks each weighing 80 tonnes had also been
built and supplied to Pacific Nuclear Transport Ltd. The units were fitted
with shock absorbers at both ends and mounted on steel transport frames
and were ultimately to be used in conjunction with purpose built ships to
transport irradiated nuclear fuel from Japan to Sellafield.

In 1983 the Technical Computer Department under its new title of
Whessoe Technical Computer Systems (WTCS) moved into a newly
built office block adjacent to the Main office and was officially opened
by Mr. Kenneth Baker the then Minister of State for Industry and
Information Technology in the October of that year. The new centre
represented an investment of over £1.5 million and was the culmination
of two decades of successful continuous development and market
exploitation by WTCS of CAD/CAM.

The purpose-designed building housed, what were at that time, some
of the most powerful main frame computers and were able to provide

One of many nuclear irradiated fuel transport flasks for B.N.F.L. at Sellafield, manufactured by Whessoe Darlington.

a service to meet both the Group's requirements and those of external customers, including engineering design, finance, planning and data retrieval and specialist graphics applications. A major feature being the bureau usage of the Whessoe developed, and now internationally famous, Pipe-stressing program (PSA5) and the Pressure Vessel Design program (PVE5) for the energy and process engineering industries.

The new headquarters with a staff of sixty, a high proportion being graduates with disciplines ranging across engineering, physics, mathematics and computer science, brought together all WTCS activities from System Design to Sales and Customer Service functions and is equipped with special demonstration and training rooms.

Two new business ventures were introduced as part of an ambitious five year business plan.

Expert Information Systems (EXIS) was set up and operated from London as a Divison of WTCS. One of its products was a new form of on-line information service which provided a data base covering regulatory information on the transportation and handling of hazardous

*Whessoe Computer Systems new office block opened in 1985 on
Whessoe's head office site at Darlington.*

materials. It could be accessed via most computer terminals over the
public telephone system and covered the International Maritime
Dangerous Goods Code, Medical First Aid Guide and Emergency
Schedules.

This was seen as an essential requirement in view of the hazardous
materials, particularly chemicals, which are continuously being moved
across country by road, rail and by air. It gives accident emergency
crews access to vital information at a moment's notice and by 1986 it
was connected to thirty-two countries covering transport regulations
and emergency response schedules.

Closer to home EXIS is in use at Gatwick Airport where, in common
with other airports, dangerous goods in air cargo and in connection
with airport operation are a growing problem.

To show the system's capabilities a 'live' incident was staged with
the Kent Police and Fire Brigade. An overturned tanker was set on fire
and the attending police patrol obtained EXIS computer print-out
instructions at the scene via a cellular phone and portable terminal.
The incident was shown nationally on Independent Television and
generated a lot of interest and business. Exis was eventually sold off
by Whessoe but is still operating world wide as a highly valued system.

Throughout the decade of the eighties the one Group Company that had a relatively stable order book and profit level was Whessoe Systems and Controls. It had none of the high publicity of the nuclear and hydro-electric projects but it proved itself to be a stabilizing influence on the Groups' activities and was eventually to be the linchpin of a swing away from Heavy Engineering to Light Engineering, giving a new direction to the Whessoe Group.

The Company has a major commitment to Research and Development and in order to expand this area and develop new systems the decision was taken to relocate their Works and Offices from the main Darlington site to provide a more modern facility that could do justice to the rapidly expanding Instrumentation and Control business. In 1989 £3.5 million was invested in a new purpose built, 420,000 square foot centre at Newton Aycliffe some 5 miles north of Darlington.

In the relating of Whessoe's fortunes during the 1980s I have as yet made only passing reference to the Group's involvement in the Off-shore Oil Industry. This has been deliberate as in my opinion it deserves a separate and special mention and some prominence—if only because I spent most of the decade at Dock Point in what was to be probably the most stressful but enjoyable period of my career.

Prior to 1982 I had had no personal involvement in Dock Point which was considered to be an Outside Erection site, an area of activity to which, if you recall, I had a particular aversion. It will be useful, however, briefly to return to the development of the site in its early stages.

In 1956 approximately $3\frac{1}{2}$ acres of land were purchased as a small construction site with easy access for river load-outs. A notable contract was for the construction of cylindrical hull sections for the Polaris submarines, using Whessoe's acclaimed pressure vessel experience.

In 1972 a second area, taking in the Point flanking the Middlesbrough Dock entrance, was acquired increasing the site area to 7 acres. On this increased area the first concrete access roads and two heavy concrete fabrication areas, together with all the site services and power distribution to service 100 welders were installed.

This represented the first stage of a facility for work related to Off-shore Platforms. Eventually a load-out jetty with a 100 ft. wide

*Aerial view of the Whessoe Offshore Facility (Dock Point) showing a
module loaded out onto a barge in the new berthing facility
opened in 1985.*

frontage and its own mooring dolphin in the river was developed at
the Point. This became necessary as Off-shore components were rapidly
exceeding the weights capable of being handled by the Middlesbrough
Docks. The new jetty was designed to accommodate load transfers on
to sea-going barges well in excess of the Leg Sections and Modules
envisaged at that time. It was later upgraded to take loads of 3,500
tonnes using the modern multiwheel trailers.

The next acquisition was a 10 acre section which had existing hard
standing and several large buildings suitable for the covered assembly
of larger fabrications. On this land a 200 ft. wide concrete slab was
constructed serviced by a 100 ft. high, 100 ton capacity Goliath crane.

The fourth extension to the site comprised a 14 acre section originally
used as a foundry. One of the buildings was restored and used as a
heated store and the land partly developed to the extent of hard-core
fill which allowed some degree of outside fabrication.

At this time Middlesbrough Docks were fully operational and load-outs from the jetty had to be timed very carefully to avoid the extensive river traffic entering and leaving the Docks. In later years when the Docks were closed Whessoe leased part of the land from the Port Authority and their warehouses were eventually used as stores for bonded materials and as additional fabrication shops. In the mid-eighties, therefore, Dock Point occupied some 38 acres of land which was to be used, in the main, for the now highly competitive Off-shore fabrication work.

During the three years from 1972 to 1975 work was concentrated on subcontracted components from Laing's Graythorpe Yard including Jacket Legs (up to 1,000 tons weight), flotation tanks, pile guides, nodes, and tubular sections, the type of cylindrical work Whessoe was familiar with. It wasn't until 1975 that the first Off-shore Modules were completed.

The Modules were for B.P.'s Oil Production platform *Highland One* each measuring 260 ft. long × 50 ft. wide × 36 ft. high and at 1,400 tonnes each were the heaviest loads in the world to be moved on trailers with pneumatic tyres, but were in fact to be the first of many much heavier loads in the years to come.

Over the next five years there was a mixture of structural fabrication contracts and the earlier experience on the B.P. modules helped Whessoe gain several more similar Module contracts from Shell, B.P., Chevron, Conoco and other oil majors. In the ten years 1970 to 1980 over thirty Off-shore contracts were completed with a turn-over value in excess of £50 million. The Off-shore business was fast becoming a boom market as the North Sea oil-fields were exploited.

There were now, however, many well established construction yards, particularly in Scotland, which had been specifically adapted for Off-shore work following the loss of much of the ship building work and they were turning their hands to Modules as well as Jackets. It was very difficult to obtain a continuing work load against such competition particularly in view of the cyclical nature of Off-shore oil contracts.

There were a lot of new techniques to be learned in planning for and building Modules and that was another problem. The labour force at that time was, as far as possible, recruited locally but any shortfall had to be topped up from travelling men. These men quite often gave up in mid-contract to return to their own areas as work picked up there, causing quite a problem with the continuity of particular skills on a contract. With a full Yard a labour force of around 500 to 750 was needed as well as a staff of 100.

The supply of labour became a major factor in the business and the labour force and the unions were quick to seize upon this fact.

Demands for wage increases, bonus payments and other ancillary benefits became the norm, with the withdrawal of their labour at a critical part of a contract being a constant threat.

As I have mentioned before, site activities around Teesside were very high in the late 1970s what with the Graythorpe Yard and the construction of the chemical complex at Seal Sands. It soon became a question of who could afford to pay the most for skilled labour in order to meet the contract completion dates demanded by the oil companies and who was prepared to pay excessive completion bonuses in order to retain labour on-site until that completion. The Industrial Relations Manager certainly earned his keep in those days.

During this period of Dock Point development the Yard was run as any other site establishment and managed from Darlington as part of the Construction Division.

It was not, and could not, at that time, be run as a factory. All of the final assemblies of large modules were being conducted in open areas with makeshift temporary covers leaving work open to the vagaries of the weather. Dock Point at that time was not an easy place to work and was looked upon by many workmen and staff, closeted in their warm work areas at Darlington, as being equivalent to Siberia.

With the award of the A.G.R. Nuclear contract in 1979 and the decision to build the Gas Baffles and other items in modular form at Dock Point things had to change. The erection of the very large Fabric-ation shops, fully lit and heated started to give the place more of a stable factory atmosphere. With a guarantee of almost four years of continuous employment the labour force settled down considerably, although it was always referred to by the experienced as the "sleeping tiger"—never knowing when it would awaken and strike again.

Halfway through the Nuclear shop-work in 1981 the site work was starting to open up at Heysham and Torness, the locations for the new Reactors. It was realized that to maintain full work loads at Darlington and Dock Point after the completion of the Nuclear shop-work serious thought would have to be given to other markets now.

It was decided that Dock Point's Off-shore activities should be marketed more enthusiastically. A comprehensive marketing exercise was set up to convince the oil companies of Whessoe's new capabilities and dedication to Off-shore work and how it could now benefit from the new workshops built specifically for the Nuclear work and the more modern facility that was now available.

It soon became apparent that Off-shore projects were going to be far more extensive than previous contracts, with fabrication programmes of up to two years duration and the oil companies were demanding that specific project teams and multidiscipline labour forces be dedicated to their particular contract. Another of their main prerequisites was that a fabrication facility had to be run, and, seen to be run, as a self sufficient company with permanent staff and management.

With this in mind, in December 1981, Whessoe were awarded a contract by British Gas for the construction of four Power Production and Process modules for their Rough Field Gas Project valued at that time at £10 million. This obviously had to be run in parallel with the A.G.R. contract but be entirely separate.

Dock Point was still being run as an erection site and the current manager was an experienced site engineer who was badly needed to head up the Heysham Nuclear construction team. The Whessoe Construction Manager at that time, John Pool, was responsible to the Whessoe Construction Director for all U.K. sites including Dock Point but he was only able to visit the Yard about once a week.

The A.G.R. contract was being run by Cliff Glasper a Project Engineer transferred from Darlington where he had been involved in the original design work. The Module contract was to be run by Trevor Brown an experienced Project Manager with several years service at

Dock Point. It was obvious, however, that a full time Facility Manager was necessary to co-ordinate all of the site work and to turn Dock Point into a self sufficient Yard as required by the oil companies as well as ensuring that Whessoe's best interests were being served at all times.

At this time I was still the Contracts Manager at Darlington, well settled into the routine contract negotiations following my visit to Mexico and enjoying a relatively stable and satisfactory career with the possibility of further promotion in the years to come. It is at this stage that something always seems to turn up to change things—sometimes for the better—sometimes not.

Ron Bishop the Managing Director of Whessoe Heavy Engineering offered me the position of Manager, Dock Point, with full responsibility for the running of the Yard in all its aspects. I would report directly to John Pool whose visits to Dock Point would still only be fleeting.

My first thoughts were "Siberia! where had I gone wrong?" Although I had the good sense to keep my thoughts to myself.

Despite the adverse publicity the Site had generated at Darlington the prospects were good. Another immediate promotion with the knowledge that eventually it was hoped to turn Dock Point into a subsidiary company in its own right with the prospects of a Directorship hovering somewhere in the background. Set against all of this was the fact that I knew next to nothing about Off-shore activities, had never been directly involved with Industrial Relations problems and didn't know many of the staff or any of the work force. But what a challenge. There was really only one decision to make. I started at Dock Point on 4th May 1982.

The designs of Off-shore Oil and Gas platforms are very complex and involved. The Jacket or Platform itself is a tubular structure weighing up to 15,000 tonnes and more and it is designed to be fastened to the sea bed with tubular piles and remain stable in water depths up to 300 metres.

On top of this platform the operating "factory" is lifted into position and welded down. The "factory" is usually made up of several packages or modules, each containing a fully equipped and working unit. It may

A 1,000 ton lower leg section for the B.P. Forties Field Offshore platform being prepared for load-out at Whessoe's Offshore facility.

be a compressor station, a computer room, oil storage and treatment plant, drilling equipment or an accommodation unit with its own bedrooms, canteen, cinema, recreation room and radio station.

The larger Jackets have, historically, been made at large coastal yards in Scotland and the modules generally at east coast yards particularly in the Tyne, Tees and Lowestoft areas. With work being spread over several manufacturers it was essential that the manufacturing tolerances were very tight so that units made on one yard slotted together with units made elsewhere.

There were really three criteria for modules:
1. They had to Work.
2. They had to Fit.
3. They had to be on Time.

and this meant extensive investment in experienced engineers, craftsmen, quality control, computerized planning and project management.

All of this I had to learn and learn quickly and I did this by stepping in as the "shadow" Project Manager on the British Gas contract alongside Trevor Brown, who was a tremendous help to me for the duration of the contract. In my opinion there is no better way of learning than doing.

With the Nuclear contract well in hand and recruitment being organized for the British Gas Project there was a total labour force of around 400 and a staff of 90 on the Yard at that time, but this was to build up to a peak of close on a thousand men.

The Rough Field contract was programmed to take 18 months to complete. In the event took two years with many ups and downs. In their haste to book Yard capacity and reserve Off-shore heavy lift cranes and barges, which were at a premium, the customer had not completed the detailed design and material ordering before placing the fabrication contract. The project consequently suffered from an inordinate number of design changes as the practicalities of manufacture proved some of the design work to be impracticable. It also suffered from material delays, particularly pipework and valves which are historically 'free issue' to the fabricator. In fact all materials other than secondary steel and consumables are supplied by the customer on a bulk purchase basis.

It is very rare that a Module Fabricator has on its books all of the disciplines necessary to fabricate and assemble a complete module. The final detail designs and drawings are generally completed by the Fabricator's own team and they also employ all of the structural disciplines necessary to build the module's framework. This is then shotblasted and painted with several coats of special paint to provide the protection against the North Sea's corrosive environment, usually by a sub-contractor. When it comes to the fit-out, that is the installation of plant and equipment and all of the process pipework and electrical cabling, once again it is usually sub-contracted and during this fit-out phase there can be as many as 500 additional men on the site. The work areas for these men have to be carefully planned and co-ordinated to minimise interference and delays.

If a sub-contractor is delayed due to deficiencies of the customer, fabricator or other sub-contractors, claims are generated for delay payments and reimbursement of standing costs. The pipework delays caused such a problem and in order to complete the contract within a reasonable period the work had to be carried out on a multiple shift pattern and with the input of additional labour often working in an uneconomical way. In the Off-shore business one was expected to get on with the job and worry about the payment later, which was all right for the customer but not an ideal situation for a fabricator with high overheads to cover and the need for profit to survive.

In the event an Acceleration Strategy was negotiated with British Gas which guaranteed payment for all work done. The justification for this necessitated teams of planners and quantity surveyors on both sides to monitor and record changes and extras.

The contract was finally completed to the satisfaction of all parties and the four modules were loaded out and sailed away to be installed on the Jacket located off the west coast of England.

This account hopefully shows the complexity of the module building business with the involvement of so many disciplines which include, designers, draughtsmen, electrical and piping engineers, planners, estimators, supervisors, yard managers, welders, platers, drillers, fitters, electricians, pipefitters, insulators, shotblasters and painters as well as quality control engineers, administration staff, storekeepers and security staff.

It was the Project Manager's responsibility to control all of this in addition to representing the Company at meetings with all levels of the customer's staff and representatives both on and off site.

A most exacting job but full of excitement and interest and personal satisfaction as these mammoth structures were completed.

Interspersed with the activities of Project Management was the need for me to be involved in other aspects of the business, particularly Industrial Relations which could be very volatile.

Fortunately for me by 1982 labour problems had settled down somewhat, most of the major site contracts, other than the Nuclear contracts
were coming to completion. The chemical complexes at Seal Sands
were commissioned and working. Laing's Graythorpe Yard was closed
and the itinerant labour forces had moved back to their own areas
looking for work closer to home. The skilled craftsmen working on
our yard were now all from the Teesside area. There had been an almost
national agreement that construction sites would use local labour
wherever possible to maintain a reasonable level of employment in
each region. The men had families and mortgages on Teesside and
were anxious to work locally for as long as possible, which, in some
respects, could have led to the situation of the 1930s where the workforce
had a total dependency upon Management. This of course was not the
case in 1980. The unions still had a strong voice and could make or
break an Off-shore Yard if relations were allowed to break down close
to sail-away times, the achievement of which were vital for the financial
security of the Yard and all those dependent upon it.

There were five separate craft unions operating on Dock Point plus
the staff and supervisory union. Each union had one or two representatives addressing the business in hand on the side. My first series of
meetings with these men, despite the support of the Industrial Relations
Manager, was a most interesting period.

The fact that I had served my time on the shop floor and had been
a union member for many years cut no ice. I was still a Manager, one
of "Them". For many months it became a mini-battle, with the shop
stewards, seeing how far they could push the new Manager and what
new concessions they could win. Ten years later I'm still not sure who
won what! One thing I did learn though was never to underestimate a
shop steward. Many of them were just good tradesmen trying to make
the best of their lives and jobs and were never really a threat. But,
there were always one or two who were really smart with carefully
calculated thoughts and a quick turn of phrase and they were the ones
to watch.

Humour, however, always found a way into industrial relations and
the men never missed an opportunity for a wind-up. I can recall one

occasion when senior visitors were coming onto the Yard prior to placing an order. The men had been asked to ensure that they were up and working immediately after the mid-morning break when the visitors were due. When we entered the shop there was a cathedral stillness and not a man in sight. Then, through the side door, with immaculate timing, came all the welders in single file singing *"Hi! Ho! Hi! Ho! it's off to work we go"* to the considerable amusement of the visitors and to my immense relief.

With a constantly changing work force, getting to know everyone on the Yard was also a problem. With the cyclical nature of the Off-shore Industry, as a contract came to completion there was usually a void of about three months before other activity could start. Even if there was a follow on contract there were many weeks of planning and material procurement before any steel could be cut. During these periods it became necessary to lay-off much of the surplus labour, leaving probably a core of about 100 to 120 tradesmen. This core force had been with Whessoe for many years and it was usually easy to recognize them amongst the hundreds when the site was busy.

The staff were also recruited in accordance with the workload so again it was difficult to recognize other than the regulars. Despite all of the movement, people came to look upon the Whessoe Yard as a reasonable place to work and were always ready to return even if they had jobs at other Yards at the time.

The place operated as a closely knit team. Everyone seemed to know instinctively what to do at any point in a contract and accepted the need to work many excessive hours to get a job done. This applied particularly to senior engineers and managers who were not paid for overtime but nevertheless never rushed to clock out and always started earlier than they need. I can remember calling meetings at crisis periods that went on until the early hours of the morning and still they were back to work on time ready to resolve another problem, of which there was always a plentiful supply.

There had previously been a feeling of isolation from Head Office at Darlington and people felt ignored, but as the workload built up we were able to introduce many social evenings and competitive sports with and against the customer's resident team of engineers and we felt we didn't need anyone else. To me the place became my second family and more often than not I spent more time there than at home.

As the British Gas Module contract was completed it became necessary to seek out new contracts to take up the vacant capacity. Fortunately at that time, unlike other Yards, we had the base load of Nuclear work to keep us going but we couldn't rely on that for ever and 1985 would see the end of that work at Dock Point.

Within weeks we were fortunate to secure a contract for some small but complex modules for Shell U.K. Exploration's Fulmar Field. This was followed by some Sub-Sea Junctions with protective frameworks which would be located on the sea bed and welded into existing pipelines to provide access from other Platform flow lines. The tolerances on these units were particularly tight as all the fitting and final welding had to be done sub-sea.

It was after the successful completion of these Junctions that I had my first Off-shore visit to the Fulmar Platform 160 miles east of Aberdeen. A Shell helicopter took four of us to the "Uncle John" diving ship from which the Sub-Sea Junctions had been laid. The sea was very rough at the time but the ship was controlled by computer-operated jet propulsion units which kept the deck level and stable under almost any conditions. We were to witness the hyperbaric welding of the pipe junctions. The existing pipeline had been cut and the Junctions installed and piled to the sea bed ready for welding by divers operating from a diving bell and a hyperbaric chamber.

The diving bell was a two man unit with an open bottom. The inside of the bell was kept at a constant positive pressure by the injection of a breathable gas-air mixture which kept the sea water from entering and the divers were able to sit with their feet virtually dangling in the water—simple but clever.

The bell was lowered onto the Hyperbaric chamber, which was a large open-bottomed structure straddling the pipeline and resting on the sea bed.

Once again, a constant positive pressure kept the water out and allowed the diver to work without any breathing apparatus even at depths of 400 feet. One of the divers entered the chamber from the bell which clamped onto and sealed itself to the chamber. (A second diver always remained in the bell for safety reasons.) Once inside the chamber the diver, who was also a qualified welder, set about grinding the pipe ends and welding the seams as if he was in a normal workshop on dry land. No breathing apparatus was necessary and he worked almost unhindered. The pipework incidentally was 20 in. diameter and over 2 in. thick and the weld required many non-destructive tests to meet the specification requirements.We all sat in relative comfort in the ship watching all this work going on at the sea bed on a large screen with pictures being constantly fed by remote operated cameras within the chamber. The welder, well aware he was being watched, performed several little song and dance acts, like any prima donna, to demonstrate his freedom of movement and apparent lack of concern about his environment.

From the Uncle John we were taken by helicopter again to the Fulmar 'A' Gas platform to view the 500 tonne Molecular Sieve module which had been lifted into position and welded to the side of the platform.

In some of the older oil and gas fields, sea water is pumped into the well to maintain an economic output. Over a period of time a biological reaction leads to the formation of highly corrosive hydrogen sulphide (sour gas) which can do tremendous damage to pipelines and equipment. Shell designed the Sieve Module to treat the gas as it came out of the well, obviating the need for expensive stainless steel pipelines to St. Fergus Terminal, 180 miles from the platform.

The module involved very complex pipework in duplex materials which was installed and welded at Dock Point by Taylor Warren a local piping contractor in which Whessoe had acquired a 75 per cent interest. Once again, free issue piping materials delayed the programme but, by judicious shift working, it went out on the planned completion date.

Another unique structural contract undertaken was the fabrication and erection of a 58 metre high Flare Tower for the Morecambe Bay Gas Field Development of British Gas. The Jacket which dwarfed the

The 850 ton Tripod Flare Tower for British Gas, Morecambe Bay being prepared for load-out at Whessoe Off-shore. The structure, 190 ft. high, was the tallest structure to be moved out of the Tees Estuary.

adjacent workshops was built and assembled entirely in the vertical position from component parts fabricated at Dock Point and Whessoe Darlington.

The structure which was of tripod design measuring 28.7 metres at the base and weighing 850 tonnes was moved onto a sea-going barge using multiwheel trailers and was the tallest steel structure ever to have been moved out of the Tees Estuary. At one stage it had to negotiate a main overhead power cable across the river Tees and to provide the clearance the barge was ballasted to almost negative buoyancy and moved out on an ebb tide.

The satisfactory conclusion of recent off-shore contracts for Shell encouraged them to place another order worth £12 million for three Modules and a Vent Tower for installation on a Gas platform located in the southern North Sea about 120 miles off the Norfolk coast.

It was known as the South East Indefatigable or S.E. Inde contract and was the first of many of a new type of module design, whereby several of the smaller service modules were combined into one large package which then formed the base or Cellar Deck for the platform.

In this instance the Cellar Deck which was over 230 ft. (70m) long and weighed 1,750 tonnes, contained air compressors and drier packages, water separators, heat exchangers, pumps and pressure vessels with all the associated pipework and electrics.

In addition there were two other modules, a Power Generation Module with the turbine generators to supply power to the whole platform, weighing 1,050 tonnes and a Gas Treatment Module weighing 1,375 tonnes.

The contract provided employment for over 700 men and was completed on time, proving to be another very satisfactory contract for both Whessoe and Shell.

In view of the obvious cost savings to the oil companies in producing larger single modules and with the knowledge that they were heading in that direction, Whessoe management deemed it prudent to invest over £2 million in a new load-out facility at the west end of the site that could accommodate the largest foreseeable off-shore structures. It was completed in October 1985 and officially opened by the Rt. Hon. Sir Alick Buchanan-Smith the then Minister of State for Energy.

The load-out of the Cellar Deck which, with all its support steelwork, weighed almost 2,000 tonnes brought the new jetty into operation for the first time.

The load-out of any structure from solid concrete onto a flat steel barge anchored in deep water is a specialist operation. The trailers designed to carry the large loads had several hundred wheels and multiple self-adjusting axles to keep the load level at all times. On later versions the axles were computer controlled.

As the front axles moved from land to water the barge had to be ballasted to counteract the load on the front of the barge and this again became computerized so that pumps were constantly pumping ballast water in and out of the barge's hull as the load's position changed.

Once the module was on the barge it was jacked onto support steelwork and the trailers moved back onto the shore. The steelwork was then welded down so that the module became an integral part of the barge, making it safe for sailing around the stormy North Sea coast.

The new jetty although designed for loads of 5,000 tonnes was capable of taking up to 10,000 tonnes provided it could be spread over

a larger area when being moved onto the barge. It was so designed
that the largest ocean-going barge could be berthed within Whessoe
land with a complete lack of penetration into the deep navigable channel
of the river Tees. It was acknowledged to be the best berthing facility
on the Tees and was eventually instrumental in helping us win the
largest Off-shore contract ever awarded to the Tees.

At the time of this increase in off-shore activity, changes were again
taking place within the Whessoe Heavy Engineering organization. In
September 1985 responsibility for U.K. construction and all manufacturing at Darlington was combined into one Division under Alan Rowley
as Director and General Manager.

All Overseas and Off-shore operations were also combined into one
Division under Frank Middlemiss as Director and General Manager.

Two months later in October 1985 Dock Point was recognized as a
viable Company in its own right and became Whessoe Off-shore
Limited, with Frank Middlemiss as Chairman, John Pool, Managing
Director, Ken Duffield, Finance Director and myself as Operations
Director.

Coincidentally, with this change, we successfully negotiated two
unique contracts. One was for a £5 million, 80 berth Accommodation
Module to replace the existing module which had seen ten years' service
on Shell's Auk Field Platform. This contract was unique in that it was,
for the first time, negotiated directly with Shell's Aberdeen office, not
London, on a fixed price basis and was the first Accommodation Module
we had ever tackled.

It was virtually a small hotel with accommodation for 80 men and
women, it had its own galley and dining room, recreation room, cinema,
medical room, radio room and helicopter deck and was fully lit and
air conditioned. Although the structural framework was similar to
previous modules the internals were totally different, requiring different
skills and standards of quality control and cleanliness.

The contract was taken as a 'learning curve' with an expectation of
a 'break even' or 'small loss' situation at the end. In the event market
forces within the North Sea oil industry caused a drop in oil prices
from around $25 per barrel to $15 per barrel which was not considered

to be a viable operating price level and Shell like all other oil companies at that time clamped down on spending and investments.

Although the contract was on a fixed price basis there were countless design changes and extras that under normal circumstances would have been negotiated on a reasonable basis. But Shell took a very firm line and after months of negotiation, taken almost to litigation level, we came away in 1987 with a substantial loss on the contract. Shell finally decided against installing the module on the Auk platform and it was stored on Dock Point for three years until 1990 with the intention of using it on a later project. The negotiated cost to Shell for the storage and maintenance helping us to recover a major part of the original loss.

The other unique contract was for £32 million of modules for the Shell Eider Field in the North Sea, 117 miles north-east of the Shetlands. The contract was won against fierce competition. It was one of the largest module contracts ever to be awarded to a single fabricator and was certainly the largest single contract ever secured by Whessoe Off-shore, even taking their share of the nuclear contract into account.

Tendering for Off-shore contracts is a very exacting business. The inquiry documents issued by Shell for the Eider Project, weighed nearly half a tonne, and were delivered to us in seven steel trunks. It took a team of twenty engineers and estimators eight weeks to complete the bid which had to be prepared with the most minute detail on pricing and planning and there were several weeks of negotiation in London after that to secure the contract.

Bids of this size cost contractors between £50,000 and £100,000 to prepare and one cannot afford to lose many orders on that basis, although over the years one award out of every ten tenders submitted was about the norm.

There were two stipulations to the contract award for Eider, one was that I had to be nominated as the Project Manager for Whessoe. The other was that we would not take on any other significant contract until such time as Shell had the confidence that the programme was being adhered to and that adequate dedicated labour was being made available for the Eider Project.

Although the inability to take on other work was a commercial restriction not normally acceptable, the contract was so large that despite the nuclear work being completed and shipped out it would in fact take up all our resources until the structural steelwork was completed.

The major part of the contract was an Integrated Deck which was a big brother to the Cellar Deck built for S.E. Inde. It contained all of the Well-head, Process, Utility and Power Generation facilities for the whole platform with enough electrical output to power up a town the size of Darlington. It had to fit directly on top of the 18,000 tonne tubular Jacket and would support the drilling module and living quarters on its roof. It weighed over 5,000 tonnes, three times the weight of the Cellar Deck and was 175 ft. (53m) long × 75 ft. (23m) wide × 42 ft. (13m) high.

In addition to the Integrated Deck the contract called for a drilling support module weighing 2,600 tonnes and a derrick module complete with all the operational drilling equipment, weighing 1,400 tonnes.

It was a thirty month contract and was to employ 1,500 people at its peak, all recruited locally.

To manage the project our own team consisted of over 100 engineers, planners, quantity surveyors and draughtsmen. Shell put on site their own team of between 80 to 120 people to monitor the Project and provide the commissioning engineers at the latter end. No module fabricator had ever been faced with such a large customer representation and we had to build a two storey office block on the site, solely for their use.

Although the Project went fairly well to plan there was always a constant battle with the customer on late receipt of drawings and material, last minute design changes (8,653 were actually recorded), clash of management personalities and of course industrial relations problems. It was a full time job maintaining a balanced workload whilst still endeavouring to ensure that the workforce had a fair share of week-end overtime and that the unsocial hours of double and triple shifting were not worked by the same people all the time. With over 300 sub-contractors on site, electricians, pipefitters, painters and insulators etc, each with their own unions, the problems were further magnified in ensuring that rates of pay, overtime allocations and working

The Shell Eider Integrated Deck, 174 ft. long × 75 ft. wide × 42 ft. high and weighing in excess of 5,000 tons was the largest off-shore module to be built and loaded out by barge for the North Sea oil fields. It was placed directly on top of the jacket and supports the drilling modules and living quarters.

patterns were not too different from Whessoe labour. Altogether 90 per cent of my time, which is any Project Manager's lot, was spent in interminable meetings with Shell, subcontractors, our own team, the unions and shop stewards, trying to keep all the balls in the air.

It was in these situations that the camaraderie of the Dock Point team always surfaced, with the majority of people doing more than job descriptions specified and putting Whessoe and work before personal needs. Without that attitude these major complex contracts would never have been completed.

When the job was finally finished in 1988 over 3.5 million man-hours had been expended over the thirty month period and the value of the contract, due to changes, had escalated to £40 million.

The Eider Project had occupied most of our time and capacity but as the structural work on all three modules drew to a close and the fitting-out took preference it was time to look for other follow-on work that could utilize the boilermaker trades.

Shell were satisfied that adequate progress had been made within the bounds of the contract and released us from the contractual condition precluding us from taking on other work.

The main problem was, that with the Yard full of Shell contracts (Eider and Auk), other oil companies were reluctant to place work with us in case their contracts played second fiddle to Shell in terms of labour and other resource availability.

For some time, however, B.P. Chemicals had been planning the construction of its new Acetyls Plant at Saltend near Hull.

B.P Chemicals, historically, had suffered many industrial relations problems on their U.K. sites and in an endeavour to minimize this problem they had decided to build the whole Acetyl Plant in modular form and install the completed units onto prepared foundations with only the hook-up of pipework, electrics and instrumentation to do on site.

Our years of experience in module design and fabrication stood us in good stead when bidding for the work and we were able to offer several worthwhile suggestions on structural design and fabrication techniques which would save the customer several thousand man-hours.

An order for seven P.A.U.s (Pre-assembled units) valued at £12 million was awarded to Whessoe Off-shore in early 1988. The approximate sizes and weights of the P.A.U.s ranged from 12 ft. up to 29 ft. in length and from 16 ft. to 24 ft. in height; all the units were 14 ft. wide so that they could be shipped out from the east end jetty onto roll-on/roll-off vessels. It was the first time such a vessel had been used at Dock Point and the multiwheel trailers and tractor units were left under the P.A.U.s during transit and were used again to take them to the prepared foundations at Saltend.

The units contained vessels, pumps and columns plus interconnecting pipework and insulation. Instrument and electrical equipment, trays,

Two of seven P.A.U.s (pre-assembled units) for B.P.'s Acetyl plant at
Hull being loaded onto a roll-on/roll-off ship at Whessoe Offshore.

racks, lighting and control cables were all fitted and tested so that when
connected together on site the seven P.A.U.s would perform as a complete factory unit.

The Yard was still full but, regrettably, most of the work was being
handled by subcontractors in the fit-out stages and it had been necessary
to lay-off the majority of the Whessoe labour force and project staff,
retaining only those necessary to administer the fit-out and commercial
negotiations.

With the three Eider modules in their final stages and the Auk
accommodation module under Care and Maintenance the B.P. contract
was a welcome addition. We were able to utilize some of the labour
being released from the Eider Project, although when the Eider modules
finally sailed away from Dock Point in April 1988 they left an even
larger void on the Yard.

Coincidental with this vacant capacity there was a lull in the placement of orders by the oil companies. The only large contract available was for Shell-Kittiwake another major project, bigger even than Eider, but this was placed on the Tyne where yards were also empty.

For almost seven years Whessoe Off-shore had been working at full capacity and we had been fortunate not to have seen the troughs that other fabricators had, thanks, to a large extent, to the nuclear work. We had been equally fortunate to have obtained the B.P. land based contract which provided limited activity into 1989, but the long-term future did not look so bright.

Business consultants had recommended that the continuation of Off-shore work be given serious consideration in view of the very high overhead cost of running such a facility without a guaranteed continuous work load. But we were determined to make a go of the place and continued to search for new work.

By October 1988 we had reduced down to below our normal core labour force but retained enough to remain a viable facility. At this point John Pool the M.D. took early retirement and I took over as Director and General Manager with most of my challenging work on Eider behind me.

Within two months the Shell Kittiwake team decided to use the stored Auk accommodation module on their own platform. This necessitated a major modification and refurbishment programme to the module entailing the strengthening and re-positioning of the Helideck and the fitting of additional walkways, handrailing and bumper systems. The telecommunication, fire and gas detection as well the public address systems also had to be extensively modified and this work, valued at about £2 million, was awarded to Whessoe Off-shore with a planned completion of mid May 1989.

This was still not enough to keep us going and for almost 9 months we worked to win more contracts for the Yard, travelling continuously to give presentations of our abilities to almost every oil company and design house in the London and Aberdeen centres of business, hoping to sell our capacity and experience. There appeared to be plenty of projects on the stocks but with oil prices at an all time low they were being held back until 1990 or even 1991 and the smaller contracts being released were too small to enable us to recover our overheads on a facility costing nearly £2 million a year to run even at low capacity.

At the end of April 1989 the decision was taken to withdraw from the Off-shore scene and close Dock Point. This meant the loss of jobs for the remaining 100 people, the majority of whom had been with Whessoe for most of their working lives, a most traumatic time for them, having worked so hard to stay in business.

The decision in hindsight proved to be the right one from a financial stand-point but understandably was difficult to accept at that time, as indeed all job losses had been throughout the Group. At the risk of repeating myself, the period at Dock Point had undeniably been the most interesting and enjoyable of my working life and it was almost like losing a family and a home. The saddest time being the final days saying goodbye to everyone and seeing all the plant and equipment that had served us so well being auctioned off.

There was still some work outstanding on the accommodation module, however, and a small team stayed on to complete the work before the Yard was finally closed for good at the end of 1989.

With so much experience behind them most of the project staff fortunately obtained work fairly quickly elsewhere, particularly on the Tyne. At about that time when I had resigned myself to early retirement I was asked if I would stay on to help develop the newly formed Whessoe Projects Limited at Darlington and I returned there in July 1989.

To understand fully the changes being made to the Whessoe Group with the closure of Dock Point and the formation of Whessoe Projects we need to go back to 1986 the year that saw the commencement of a surge of organizational and managerial changes which heralded the move into the ninth period of change of Whessoe's history, from Heavy Engineering to Light Engineering.

In May 1986 George Duncan, a business man highly respected in the City, joined Whessoe Main Board as a non-executive director and in September was appointed Deputy Chairman.

On the 31st December 1986 Ron Bishop, Managing Director of Whessoe Heavy Engineering, retired having reached the age of sixty-five after thirty-six years of service with the Company. He joined Whessoe in 1947 from Clare College, Cambridge, where he took an Engineering degree and, apart from three years in Canada, spent the rest of his working life at Whessoe as Welding Engineer, General Manager R. & D., Technical Director and Managing Director of Whessoe Heavy Engineering. He was appointed to the Main Board in 1971 and was also Chairman of W.T.C.S. and Whessoe Ireland, Director of W.S. & C., T.N.P.G. and the British Nuclear Associates Board.

Ron Bishop made a significant contribution to Whessoe's engineering capability during his career particularly in the nuclear field for which he was awarded the C.B.E. in the 1987 Queen's Birthday Honours List. He remained on the Whessoe Board as a non-executive Director and also remained a member of the Council of the Welding Institute and Chairman of the U.K. Committee of the International Institute of Welding.

Following his retirement the Whessoe Group was decentralized into separate limited companies comprising:

W.H.E.L. (Whessoe Heavy Engineering Ltd.)

W.O.S.L. (Whessoe Offshore Ltd.)

W.O.L. (Whessoe Overseas Ltd.)

W.(I).L. (Whessoe Ireland Ltd.)

W.T.C.S. (Whessoe Tech. Computer Systems.)

Aiton (Derby and Australia)

W.S.& C. (Whessoe Systems & Controls.)

all Managing Directors reporting directly to Bill Smart the Group Chief Executive.

In 1987 due to the generally depressed demand for heavy engineering products a rationalization to reduce Group costs was carried out and over 450 redundancies were announced from Aiton and Darlington.

In May 1987 Lord Errol of Hale retired after twenty-two years as a Director of Whessoe, the last seventeen years as Chairman. He was succeeded by George Duncan the Deputy Chairman.

In June 1987 Alan Coultas the M.D. of W.T.C.S. left to set up his own Company and Keith Berry took over as Director & General Manager.

Ian Paterson M.D. of Aiton retired through ill health and was succeeded by Donald Wood in January 1988.

April 1988 saw the appointment of Chris Fleetwood as Group Financial Director and in the same month Alan Rowley the Managing Director of Whessoe Heavy Engineering took early retirement after thirty-nine years service. He started in 1949 as a Project design engineer, in 1959 he became Chief Engineer—Storage embracing S. & J. tank fittings. He was involved in early computing within R. & D. in 1961, becoming R. & D. Manager in 1964. From 1965 to 1979 he was Engineering Manager of Whessoe Heavy and became Director of the Nuclear Division upon the award of the Heysham and Torness A.G.R. contracts. He was appointed to the Main Board in 1984

Although his leaving had no direct impact on the recent overall organizational changes I would hesitate to leave this section of the history without mentioning R.S. (Dick) Wilson. Dick, like many others, spent most of his working life at Whessoe and was a respected and popular member of the staff with a phenomenal memory and an uncanny knack of being able to put his finger on the root cause of many commercial and contractual problems.

His career was quite varied. Having completed an apprenticeship at Jos. Cook's colliery engineers at Washington D.C. (Durham County!) he applied for a job as a draughtsman at Whessoe in 1939 but was coerced into becoming an estimator. Throughout the war years he was a cost engineer shadowing Ministry of Supply cost investigators on war contracts and was later responsible for planning the optimum allocation of rationed steel for the Works and Sites.

Post-war he specialized in the estimating of gas plant and gas-holders and then cost investigations and contract negotiation for major gas-plants.

In 1950 he became responsible for setting up licensing agreements for Shand & Jurs fittings in Holland, France, Germany, Norway, Denmark and Italy. This was followed by extended periods in the U.S.A., India and Yugoslavia investigating Econotherm heaters. M. & J. Valves and special tankage contracts.

He was successively Chief Estimator, Northern Sales Manager, then Group Estimating Manager, moving on to become General Manager— Finance & Central Planning, finishing as Commercial Director. He was appointed to the Main board in 1978 and retired at the age of 65 in 1983 after forty-three years' service with the Company.

Having completed the first phase of cost reduction with the redundancies at Aiton and Darlington the Company aimed at formulating a strategy for the future course and development of the Group's business. To assist in this task the services of Bain & Co. the Business Consultants were engaged and they spent several months reviewing all areas of activity before making their recommendations to the Board.

Their views apparently coincided to some extent with those of the Executive Management and not long after this, further rationalization activities took place with the merging of Manufacturing, Projects and U.K. and Overseas construction into a new Company. Whessoe Projects Limited, which effectively replaced Whessoe Heavy Engineering Ltd. and Whessoe Overseas Ltd. Frank Middlemiss was appointed Managing Director of this new Company although he himself was due to retire in April 1989 and a search was put in hand to identify his replacement prior to that time.

In order to provide a sound and profitable footing for the new company the Darlington Works fabrication and manufacturing facilities were to operate on a much reduced scale concentrating mainly upon completing on-going contracts, particularly those supporting site onstruction work at home and overseas.

Obviously this contraction of activity involved further job losses and by the end of December 1989 seventy staff and one hundred works employees had been made redundant. Once again a regrettable necessity but it was essential that Whessoe Projects should move forward unencumbered by excess Works manufacturing capacity.

The formation of Whessoe Projects was the first public indication of a significant change in Whessoe's future development.

George Duncan when first appointed a non-executive director at Whessoe in 1986 had been disturbed by two factors. First, at the age of 53, he was the youngest man in the boardroom. Second, and more serious, the Company had no Finance Director. One of his first actions when appointed Chairman in 1987 was to search out and appoint Chris Fleetwood as Whessoe's first Finance Director for more than ten years. It was not long before he was appointed Group Managing Director prepared to succeed Bill Smart as Chief Executive upon his retirement in December 1989.

Chris Fleetwood, himself only 38 years of age, was charged with leading the Company out of impending financial crisis. Within nine months he had recruited his own young executive team. John Samuel as Finance Director, Ken Mullen as Company Secretary and legal adviser, replacing George Renwick who retired after more than twenty years' service and Clive Dennis taking over from Frank Middlemiss to run what was the core but troubled heavy engineering operation. All were in their early thirties or early forties.

One of Clive Dennis' first actions after taking over as Managing Director of Whessoe Projects was to organize it into two business areas, Manufacturing Group and Projects Group. This division of activity was made in June 1989.

Within weeks of my return to Darlington in the July the decision had been taken to phase out completely the manufacturing arm. The performance of the manufacturing operation had continued to be unsatisfactory in spite of attempts to restructure the business. A major problem had been the low level of demand and a bleak outlook for future sales. The market for the products that could be fabricated profitably was limited and competition was intense.

The closure of such a labour intensive facility was neither a short nor a simple process. Contracts had to be completed for both shop-built and site-built contracts. Detailed negotiations were required with shop floor and staff unions on the phasing out of the 300 personnel in such a way as to provide balanced activity on current contracts yet still allow a degree of latitude if people had opportunities to take up other jobs elsewhere and wished to leave early. Like the Off-shore Yard the people left tended to be long service loyal employees who warranted special treatment in job counselling and redundancy payments.

The complete closure of the Works took over a year. It was June 1990 before the plant and equipment were put up for sale by public auction and another major part of Whessoe's history was brought to a close.

My very recent experience in the closing of a Whessoe facility meant that once again I was involved in organizing a redundancy programme, mainly with the staff personnel, although admittedly without the direct personal contact this time.

The cataloguing of all the plant and equipment for sale was also a time consuming procedure particularly as we had to ensure that site plant and small tools for use on Whessoe Projects contracts was retained and stored separately.

In parallel with all this, of course, was the need to conclude contractual negotiations on manufacturing contracts as they were completed and shipped out and to introduce autonomous financial and business control systems so that Whessoe Projects Ltd. could be a self sufficient and profitable part of the Whessoe Group.

12

The Nineteen Nineties

The New Projects Company set out to complete existing contracts such as the Sukkur Barrage which still had about two years to completion and also to seek out and obtain new contracts that would utilize all the retained skills and the construction plant and equipment on a profitable basis.

The closure of the fabrication facility meant that materials for tank and site-built pressure vessels had to be bought from our previous competitors, but work was in such short supply that this did not cause much of a problem. On overseas projects the practise of building temporary workshops and using local labour under expatriate supervision was maintained and proved to be very successful. Overhead costs were restricted to those in maintaining the Darlington offices and plant and equipment and of course the necessary administration staff for tendering and contract control.

With new systems in place and with a slimmed down complement of staff under the control of new management, the search for new work took the Company into many remote areas of the world. The Sukkur Barrage in Pakistan had its own share of environmental problems in a relatively remote area of the country. But the next overseas contract was even more problematic.

The Government of Mozambique were endeavouring to develop the local fishing industry around the coastal areas of the Indian Ocean and required a permanent landing jetty or fish quay to be built at the remote town of Angoche some 850 kilometres from the nearest port of Beira.

Whessoe construction engineers visited the area and submitted a bid for the design, supply, installation and commissioning of a floating jetty. The bid was successful and an order was received in early 1990

The floating jetty designed and constructed by Whessoe Projects at Angoche, Mozambique.

valued at £1.7 million for a steel access bridge on piled supports with a 60 metre long fixed section and a 70 metre long hinged section. At the end of the hinged section a floating pontoon 50 m long × 8 m wide × 4 m deep and weighing 280 tonnes had to be attached to allow for tidal movements.

The People's Republic of Mozambique is a poor tribal nation, beset by tribal warfare and the disease-ridden tsetse fly, and with very little industrial activity. The site for the new jetty was basic to say the least, causing extreme logistic problems in material delivery and fabrication work.

The project on site was run by Wally Jordan one of Whessoe's most senior construction supervisors, who seems to have been at Whessoe forever, and the labour was hired in from Pakistan.

A temporary slipway was constructed and materials virtually run up onto the beach and unloaded, a lot of it by hand. The steelwork was shipped plate small from England and the bridge and pontoon were manufactured, tested and painted on the beach at Angoche. In spite of the local difficulties the contract was completed within ten months.

Work is currently ongoing on a new contract at Matola in Mozambique covering the design, supply and construction work associated with the rehabilitation and specification upgrade of an existing Oil Products Jetty. The work comprises repairs to damaged concrete structures, the provision of new berthing dolphins, replacement of all the existing pipework and electrical systems and the supply of new fire detection and fire fighting systems.

There is also additional work to be done in the design, supply and construction of a new jetty and dolphins for grain handling operations which includes the installation of 2,000 tonnes of tubular steel piles and 6,000 m^3 of reinforced concrete.

Another remote contract site is on the volcanic Ascension Island in the south Atlantic. 1,500 miles from mainland Africa. The island which is British owned has a constantly changing population of around 1,500 made up from British expatriates, R.A.F. and U.S. Air Force personnel. The major contractor on the side is a team of B.B.C. engineers who operate their Atlantic Relay station there.

As part of the B.B.C.'s occupancy agreement they are required to operate and maintain the island's oil-fired power station. Tenders were requested from Whessoe and other major competitors for the refurbishment of the power station's ancillary systems including the drilling of wells, pipework for boiler steam, potable water and drainage, together with electrics and instrumentation for the installation of a new desalination plant.

The contract finally awarded to Whessoe was valued at £3 million and was funded by the Treasury but negotiated by B.B.C. engineers.

All materials had to be shipped in by sea and with no natural harbour all goods had to be lightered to the pier head. Personnel had to be flown in by courtesy of the R.A.F. from Brize Norton in the U.K. Supervisory staff and engineers were sent out from England but labour and administration staff came from the island of St. Helena 800 miles away.

In the latter months of 1989 and into early 1990 negotiations were going ahead for a share in the contract being placed by the Indian Government for a hydro-electric scheme similar to those previously carried out by Whessoe in Sri Lanka and Mrica. The work was finally placed with an Anglo-Swedish consortium with Scansca of Sweden being the main contractor and Boving/Whessoe being responsible again for the mechanical and hydraulic equipment.

The work site at URI is in Kashmir India on the border with Pakistan and has been the scene of extended delays due to religious/political warring between the Kashmir Hindus, Muslims and Sikh tribesmen who neither accept the territorial borders of India and Pakistan nor those of the individual religious factions.

Work did get started with the erection of fabrication shops for the rolling and welding of tunnel liners but came to a halt after the kidnapping of two Swedish engineers. The site is actually 2,000 miles north of Bombay which is the nearest sea port and all shipped-in materials must travel by road for that distance. At the peak of the uprising it was too dangerous for site personnel to travel by road and helicopter flights had to be used at all times. With the eventual return of the Swedish engineers the area settled down somewhat and work restarted.

The contract was valued at £450 million, £50 million of which was the U.K. share divided between Boving at £43 million and Whessoe £7 million.

The principle of the hydro-electric scheme is similar to previous ones with a 14 kilometre concrete lined head race tunnel from the upstream river barrage leading into an excavated surge chamber. The outlet from the chamber is split by a steel bifurcation into two 5 metre diameter power tunnels which are bored vertically downwards for 213 metres and steel lined. Each tunnel then bends at 90 degrees in the horizontal plane and each one is split again with a bifurcation leading to the four turbine generators in the power house. All of the steel tunnel liners and the bifurcations are fabricated on site by Whessoe and installed in the tunnels, which has by now become a fairly standard operation except for the fact that this time we are lining vertical tunnels, never attempted before. Whessoe engineers are, however, quite adept at overcoming those sorts of problem and the contract should proceed to plan provided the civil wars do not start up again.

Finally the largest current project and the most prestigious is for a cryogenic storage facility for the Public Gas Corporation of Greece

(DEPA). Low temperature storage design has always been one of Whessoe's strengths with much of the design technology residing with one or two highly qualified engineers.

The Greek Government was looking for competitive, high integrity designs for an L.N.G full containment storage system, readily accessible to sea-borne L.N.G. tankers.

The site chosen was the Island of Revithoussa half a kilometre off mainland Greece in the Bay of Megara with deep water access for the L.N.G. tankers.

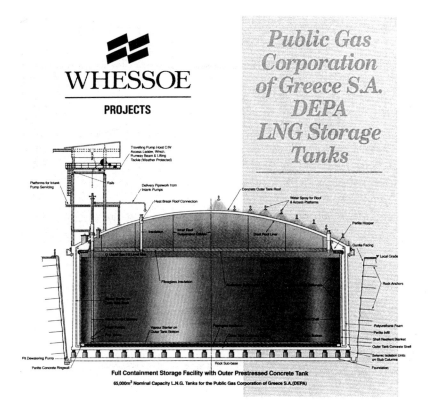

Design outline of the cryogenic storage tanks being designed and built by Whessoe Projects for the Greek Public Gas Corporation (DEPA).

The scope of work involved the design, supply and erection of two double skinned tanks, each 65.7m (215 ft.) diameter × 22.5m (74 ft.) high, each containing 65,000m³ of liquefied natural gas. (L.N.G.) to be stored at a temperature of minus 162°C. They are at the most sophisticated end of the cryogenic market.

The tanks had to be erected inside deep excavations in the island rock and had to be designed with special safety features to allow for seismic conditions, earthquakes being an ever present danger in that part of the Mediterranean.

Whessoe Projects in consortium with Dyckerhoff and Widman of Germany and Technical Union of Greece were awarded the contract, more on design credibility than price, with an overall value of £40 million, with the Whessoe element being worth £25 million. The Project is funded by the E.E.C.

The tank design is based on an outer shell of prestressed concrete 500mm thick with a domed roof 450mm thick, the inside surfaces of which are lined with a 3mm thick steel vapour barrier. The inner shell in direct contact with the refrigerated L.N.G. is made of 9 per cent nickel steel and sandwiched between the two shells is an insulation barrier of perlite and polyurethane foam.

Two exacting requirements of the design are that the tanks are to be virtually bomb proof, able to withstand missile attack and the impact of crashing helicopters and are also to be capable of resisting the effects of earthquake conditions. This is being achieved by the shells being sunk almost to their full height in the excavated rock and by the shape and thickness of the domed roof. The second criterion is being met by supporting the whole tank on specially designed seismic jacking units which isolate the tank from the effects of ground tremors during earthquake situations.

All of the civil works, including the excavations and the slipforming of the concrete shells would be carried out by Dyckerhoff the German partners. After the excavations a concrete base is to be laid for each tank and the prestressed concrete walls will be slipformed to their full height. Whessoe will then fabricate and weld into position the thin steel vapour barrier and fabricate the domed roof liner. Compressed air

Excavations for the DEPA cryogenic tanks in preparation on the Greek island of Revithoussa.

will then be injected into the tank which will raise the roof liner until it can be anchored to steel inserts in the concrete shell. With the tank still under pressure reinforcing steel will be positioned and the concrete poured to form the roof.

The 9 per cent nickel inner tank will be erected and welded inside the concrete shell with materials being passed through access slots left in the wall.

In principle, once the designs were finalized the work should have proceeded without any major problems but unfortunately the contract was delayed by almost a year due to major disagreements between Dyckerhoff and the Greek engineers on what should be the criteria for the interpretation of seismic events in order to determine the seismic loads likely to be imposed.

The delay caused by this disagreement prevented Whessoe from proceeding with the steelwork and tank design appeared unlikely to commence before the end of 1993.

The cost of such delays, of course, are enormous in terms of delayed income. Plant, equipment and personnel are prevented from moving onto other contracts and this was one of the reasons why decisions have been taken to move away from heavy engineering with its high risks and low returns.

Matters were eventually resolved by the Greek General Election in October 1993. A Socialist Government replaced the incumbent Conservative Party and as Executive Management for all Greek Power Utilities are Government appointments, the Managing Director and other main board directors of DEPA were replaced.

The new management undertook to resolve the deadlock and after a series of meetings and the resolution of the seismic design criteria it was decided that Dyckerhoff and Widman would have no further involvement in the contract.

All civil activities are being taken over by Technical Union of Greece with Whessoe Projects being responsible for all mechanical aspects, including the Seismic Isolators.

Design and construction activities have now recommenced with every endeavour being made to pull back the extended completion date.

Another arm of the current Whessoe Group is Whessoe Computing Systems Ltd. which, whilst not considered to be a strategic part of the re-formed Group, is still seen as a viable business with the ability to be self sufficient and profitable. Only 4 per cent of its business now comes direct from Group.

In its very early days Whessoe Technical Computing Department was set up to provide technical computing services to the Whessoe Group companies. Financial and Administration services were provided by a separate computer department.

At that time Technical Computing were not allowed to offer their services outside the Group as a considerable amount of Whessoe engineering expertise had been encapsulated in computer code and to offer this outside would be selling our competitive advantage.

In later years, as separate stand-alone programs were developed, particularly PSA5 for pipe stress analysis, used extensively by Aiton, the software package was offered to the U.K. market as a bureau service and became almost an over night success. External revenue built up to such an extent that the decision was taken to set up a new company, Whessoe Technical & Computing Systems Ltd. (WTCS), under the leadership of Alan Coultass with the brief to offer all its products externally.

External revenue, based mainly on this bureau service, increased substantially with the receipt of the C.A.E.M.S. contract for the Sizewell 'B' nuclear pipework programme.

In subsequent years miniaturization was reducing computers from the enormous main frames that occupied whole rooms, with only about 9 megabytes capacity, to desk top computers with up to 40 megabytes (currently 400 MB). Group companies gradually took over most of their own design and financial projects and with the loss of revenue from this and the eventual phasing out of the CAEMS contract W.T.C.S. had to look again at other sources of income.

With the arrival of a new Managing Director in May 1990 it soon became apparent that although W.T.C.S. had a competent organization and credibility within the engineering world it was not a truly commercial business and was unlikely to remain competitive in the open market without significant change. A decision was taken to reorganize and restructure the business to bring a greater commercial awareness to the Company and to strengthen the business portfolio.

In addition to installing their own accounting and office administration systems they switched to UNIX technology of computing which permits software to be used on any make of hardware thus creating a much larger market. From there, existing software packages were examined for current suitability and streamlined and updated where necessary.

Three well tried and tested design programs, PSA5 the Pipe Stressing program, PVE5 the Pressure Vessel design program and HED5 the Heat Exchanger tubesheet design program formed the basis of the new portfolio and are still proving very successful with major manufacturers such as I.C.I., BNFL, Nuclear Electric and National Power.

Two new packages have been introduced, one being a Plant Maintenance Management System WCS-PPM which is a totally integrated system for the production of practical information relating to the efficient organization of day-to-day maintenance jobs and long term Planned Maintenance.

The other is MC2000, a complete Manufacturing Management System specifically developed for the high risk made-to-order end of the manufacturing business. It is designed to take advantage of state of the art technology to give better information faster than ever before. Scheduling that previously took hours can now be done in minutes.

It covers the full range of activities from receipt of an inquiry to costing and planning the bid, executing the job and investigating resource overloads. It also covers material ordering, issuing and trace-ability records on multiple jobs on the factory floor and evaluates the impact of new work on existing in-hand contracts.

The system is now well received in the industry and is so user-friendly that it can be installed and operating in a matter of weeks rather than months or years.

With this greatly enhanced portfolio and the slimmed down organiz-ation comprising twenty-seven highly qualified graduate computer engineers, who are constantly updating and developing new systems, Whessoe Computer Systems should have a very bright future as a valuable member of the Whessoe Group. But, there was no doubt that for the Group to survive, major strategic changes had to be made and it was necessary to seek and invest in growth and to win a greater market share for current products and to develop new products to attack niche markets.

With the rapid decline of nuclear power as an energy source in the U.K., despite the Sizewell 'B' project, Aiton were already looking elsewhere for piping system work both at home and overseas and the acquisition of Connex Pipe Systems of Ohio, U.S.A., a company recog-nized throughout the world for high integrity, high performance piping fabrication, opened the way for the strategic expansion of Whessoe into the U.S. power generation market.

Connex is primarily a fabricator but the acquisition will add Aiton's design expertise to Connex's fabrication capability and enable them to offer a combined design and fabrication package in the U.S. as Aiton already does in the U.K. and of course Aiton already has considerable experience in working to U.S. standards in addition to those of the European countries.

In recognition of the importance of pipework activities within the restructured Group, Donald Wood with his vast experience in pipework engineering, particularly in the marketing field, was appointed Chairman of the new Piping Division, which now comprises Aiton U.K., Aiton Australia and Connex Pipe Systems, with specific responsibility for Divisional Marketing.

The decision was also taken to appoint Clive Dennis as Managing Director of the Piping Systems Division with responsibility for the cohesive development of the Division in terms of operational control and effectiveness and the utilization of the synergistic benefits between companies. His new role was in addition to his other responsibilities as Managing Director of Whessoe Projects Ltd.

Whessoe Systems and Controls Ltd. had already set itself up for change with its move to the new premises in 1989 and by 1990 was well on the way to coping with the demands of its ever developing market.

The move to Newton Aycliffe in 1989 had been the brain child of Bill Reeves the incumbent Managing Director who visualized an autonomous company with a single status workforce in line with the majority of their international competitors. He was supported in this concept by Malcolm Burke the Commercial Director who had been with the company, serving under the two previous managing directors, Eric Walker and Frank Teasdale, since 1971.

Bill Reeves left the company for pastures new before the finalization of the plans and Malcolm Burke took over as Managing Director and set up a project team for the development of the site and factory. The concept of a single status workforce had to be tackled early. With five separate unions controlling a complement of 60 shop floor workers it was certainly not an ideal structural base for the long-term future. The detailed negotiations with the union officials were handled by Personnel management headed up by Colin Turner the Production Director. The basis of discussion was the need to develop the long-term future of the Company requiring greater flexibility within the workforce to enhance performance and productivity.

Agreement was eventually reached that, in exchange for an offer of the same terms and conditions of employment as the staff, including sick pay, holiday pay and pensions, the shop floor workers would agree to an end to all demarcation practices. And, given adequate training, a cessation of aversarial attitudes to any new working practices considered necessary to develop the business. There has already been a great improvement in performance and productivity and therefore profitability, which has opened the way for the anticipated expansion of the Instrumentation and Controls Division as a major player in the world markets.

The main business of Whessoe Systems and Controls is the design and manufacture of static liquid measurement equipment predominantly for the petro-chemical industry. In the vanguard of this work is the development of an "Intelligent Tank Gauge" (I.T.G.)

Whesstation System of fuel level monitoring for garage forecourt storage tanks. Electronic sensors can detect even the smallest change in level.

The I.T.G. is a precision measuring system which expands on the traditional servo gauge principle to gauge accurately a wide range of parameters in a storage tank. A series of transducers contained in a microprocessor controlled head are used to measure the key aspects of the contents of the storage tank as the head it vertically profiled through the tank by the main gauge which is usually mounted on the tank roof.

The high accuracy and multiple measurement features of the I.T.G. have been designed to meet the Weights and Measures authorities of Europe, particularly of France and Holland who have probably the tightest such authorities in the world.

The high level of accuracy from a single instrument is important for the control of hydrocarbon loss across a storage or refining facility, particularly so for the American market where Environmental Protection is closely monitored.

The further development of I.T.G. is part of a major commitment that Whessoe Systems and Controls has to Research and Development and was one of the reasons for the relocation of their Works.

In their assessment of future requirements they have been contemplating for some time the wisdom of staying mainly with the petro-chemical industry. One of the major areas that would see significant investment levels in the next few years is the water industry in the run-up to and following privatization which would mean the move from the 'static' measurement of liquids to 'dynamic' measurement, cutting into another 'niche' market and becoming a world leader in overall Fluids Management.

Entry into the U.S. market is also an important development and in February 1990, to provide that entry the Whessoe Group strengthened its involvement in the Instrumentation and Controls sector by acquiring Coggins Systems Inc. based in Atlanta, U.S.A.

The company is involved in Supervisory Control and Data Acquisition Systems such as SCADA, covering a wide range of applications including water distribution, energy managements, data collection and reporting, nuclear process and pollution and environmental control.

Coggins has also carried out extensive work with the U.S. Department of Defence in connection with its strategic petroleum reserves which have recently received prominence following the Gulf crisis.

In November 1990 the Group acquired another strategic Instrument-ation and Control company—Elcon Instruments based near Milan, Italy and also in the U.S.A. Elcon is a leading designer and manufacturer of intrinsic safety instruments and barriers. These instruments are increasingly used at many industrial plants where there is a risk of fire and explosion as they are incapable of generating a spark under normal operation and can be used within a hazardous environment to fulfil any measurement or control function.

By early 1992 the acquired companies had integrated well into the Whessoe Instrumentation and Controls Division and moves were afoot to acquire Varec, a U.S. based company with products and markets which were highly complementary to the existing activities of the Group.

When negotiations were finalized and the acquisition completed the three companies operating in this field, Whessoe SA—Calais, Whessoe Systems & Controls Ltd.—U.K. and Varec, were renamed WHESSOE VAREC and now together form one of the world leaders in tank level gauging and vapour control products.

There was now a need to combine more effectively the assets and resources of the three companies, each with unique and diverse cultures, business practices and products into one cohesive organization, respon-sive to customers' needs. To market these skills and to improve the geographical coverage, Malcolm Burke was appointed as Divisional Marketing Director utilizing to the full his previous experience in this international field.

His position as Managing Director of Whessoe Varec U.K. was taken over by Colin Turner the Production Director who had been with the company since 1989. Prior to that he had been with the Management Consultancy team which helped to organize the move of Systems and Controls from Darlington to Aycliffe.

Whessoe Varec S.A. was by this time under the control of Jim Kennedy who had been transferred from Whessoe plc. following the retirement of Jean Mailliot the French Managing Director. The acquired companies remained under the direct control of their own senior manage-ment staff with each of the Managing Directors reporting directly to Chris Fleetwood the Chief Executive.

The new head office and works of Whessoe Systems and Controls (now Whessoe Varec.) at Newton Aycliffe near Darlington.

The Instrumentation and Controls Division currently has a turnover of £32 million and employs 454 people but is still looking to expand and develop both organically and by further acquisition.

In February 1993 the Whessoe Group commenced overtures for the acquisition of Autronica AS. a major instrumentation company in Norway. By the end of the financial year Whessoe had acquired virtually all of the share capital and the Norwegian Government's approval of the change of ownership was received in October 1993.

Autronica AS which is based in Trondheim, Norway, is primarily involved in the design, manufacture and distribution of maritime and industrial instrumentation and fire security systems. These are covered by two separate divisions; Marine Instrumentation and Fire Detection.

The Marine Instrumentation Division provides engine monitoring systems as well as cargo management systems based on non- intrusive radar-based level gauges for liquid measurement in storage tanks. They have also developed a radar gauge which pinpoints, for the ship's Captain, the bow, stern and beam positions of tanker vessels during berthing operations.

The Fire Detection Division produces intelligent sensors which signal the existence of fire and other potentially hazardous conditions and relays information to a central processing unit at both offshore and onshore locations.

Autronica's products are complementary to a number of those already in the Whessoe Group and represent an important expansion to the Group's activities in these areas.

With an annual turnover of £46 million sterling and an employment average in excess of 500 persons the acquisition more than doubles the turnover and employment figures of the existing Instrumentation and Controls Division.

The head office and works of Autronica AS at Trondheim, Norway.
Whessoe Plc's latest acquisition and important development of
Whessoe's Instrumentation and Controls Division.

With the move away from heavy engineering now complete and the recent acquisitions of piping and instrumentation companies, the restructuring of the Group was virtually complete and in the words of the Chief Executive "We are now an engineering group driven by profit and performance and are no longer engineering for engineering's sake."

Whessoe has adapted well to the changing industrial climate, as indeed it has been doing for the last 200 years. Over 60 per cent of its work is in overseas markets with foreign governments with payments as near as can be, guaranteed and in sterling.

The recent savage surgery in cutting out loss making manufacturing activities and the restructuring of the Group as a whole has put the Group in a cash rich situation without the crippling burden of heavy interest rates thus putting it in an advantageous position over its competitors.

Things cannot, however, be taken for granted. For any business to prosper it needs a good management team, a good workforce and a slice of good luck. With its well balanced Executive Board of two accountants and two engineers under the leadership of the Chairman, George Duncan, and a workforce which is giving of its best, the first two appear to be in place and the Group has enjoyed its share of the third.

This formula, together with the restructuring should mean that the future of the Whessoe Group in its ever changing and developing guise is as assured as possible in these uncertain economic times.

This, then, is the new look Whessoe Group—a company that recognises its proud heritage but is looking to develop its skills and reputation further in its move towards the twenty-first century.

Postscript

This summary draws to a close the current Whessoe Story complete up to December 1992. It also brings to an end my personal 50 years active association with Whessoe, having retired officially in September 1990 but working again in a consultative capacity until finally being put out to grass in April 1992.

Finally another historical achievement is worth recording. I mentioned earlier in the book my office boy associates in the 1940s. One such person was Bill Moore who has recently completed his 50 years service with the Company as a senior estimator, as indeed his father did before him, as a construction foreman. He is undoubtedly the last person in the Whessoe Group able to achieve that dubious distinction and, with me, he joins the ranks of the many long service employees who have served Whessoe over the last 200 years.

What the future holds for Whessoe is anybody's guess but I recall earlier comments made by a speaker at one of Whessoe's Annual Dinners in 1959. He reflected upon Whessoe's progress since 1790 moving from the building of one of the first steam locomotives to the construction of wind tunnels and nuclear reactors and posed the question "Who in 1790 could have envisaged work of the current magnitude and who today can envisage what Whessoe will be doing in 1990? Perhaps something to do with interplanetary space travel".

The speaker's predictions were actually fairly accurate, we have indeed, through our association with Coggins Instruments, entered into the space industry by virtue of their work on satellite tracking systems for the U.S. Government.

It is certainly very difficult to envisage what Whessoe will be doing in another fifty years, but what ever it is I have no doubt that they will be one of the leaders in the field and I for one wish all those associated with the Group, success and well being for the future.

Whessoe Group

List of Chief Executives

1790–1819	William Kitching	Owner
1819–1845	William Kitching Jnr.	Owner
1831–1882	Alfred Kitching	Partner
1862–1884	Charles Ianson	Owner
1866–1885	James Ianson	Partner
1885–1890	Alfred Edward Kitching	Owner
	Henry Kitching	Partner
1890–1913	Thomas Coates	Owner
1895–1920	H. S. Smith-Rewse	Partner
1913–1924	Alfred Tom Coates	Managing Director
1920–1955	H. G. Judd	Chairman
1925–1935	R. B. Hodgson	Managing Director
1935–1954	C. M. Spielman	Managing Director
1955–1961		Chairman
1961–1964		President
1954–1961	A. G. Grant	Managing Director
1961–1970	J. H. Lord	Chairman
1961–1963	M. H. Noone	(joint) Managing Director
	S. R. Chetwynd Archer	(joint) Managing Director
1963–1970	M. N. Noone	Managing Director
1975–1986	R. F. Bishop	Managing Director
1970–1987	Lord Erroll	Chairman
1970–1988	W. S. Smart	Chief Executive
1987–	G. S. Duncan	Chairman
1988–	C. Fleetwood	Chief Executive

Whessoe Group Companies

January 1994

Whessoe Plc	Darlington, England
Whessoe Projects Ltd.	Darlington, England
Whessoe Computer Systems Ltd.	Darlington, England
Aiton & Co.Ltd.	Derby, England
Aiton (Australia Pty.)	N.S.Wales, Australia
Connex Pipe Systems Inc.	Virginia, U.S.A.
Whessoe Varec Ltd.	Aycliffe, England
Whessoe Varec Inc.	California, U.S.A.
Whessoe Varec Sa	Calais, France
Coggin Instruments	Atlanta, U.S.A.
Elcon Instruments	Milan, Italy
Autronica As	Trondheim, Norway

Index